READY-MADE COMPANY MINUTES & RESOLUTIONS

The contents of this book have been approved by
H M Williams Chartered Certified Accountants

First edition 1998
Second edition 1999
Third edition 2005
Fourth edition 2008
Fifth edition 2009
Sixth edition 2013
Seventh edition 2015

Published by

Lawpack Publishing Limited
76-89 Alscot Road
London SE1 3AW

www.lawpack.co.uk

ISBN 9781910143254

For convenience (and for no other reason), 'him', 'he' and 'his' have been used throughout and should be read to include 'her', 'she' and 'her'.

Important facts about this Lawpack book

Lawpack publications are designed to provide authoritative and accurate information on the subject matter covered. However, neither this nor any other publication can take the place of a solicitor on important legal matters.

This Lawpack publication is sold on the understanding that the publisher, author and retailer are not engaged in rendering legal services to the reader. If legal advice or other expert assistance is required, the services of a competent professional should be sought.

The forms included in this Lawpack publication cover many everyday matters, but we cannot cater for all circumstances. If what you want is not included, we advise you to see a solicitor.

This Lawpack publication is designed for use throughout the UK, and is based on our understanding of the law as at 1 July 2015.

The information this book contains has been carefully compiled from reliable sources but its accuracy is not guaranteed as laws and regulations can change and be subject to differing interpretations as well as different dates of implementation.

As with any legal matter, common sense should determine whether you need the assistance of a solicitor rather than relying solely on the information and forms in this Lawpack book.

We strongly urge you to consult a solicitor whenever substantial amounts of money are involved, or where you do not understand the instructions or are uncertain how to complete and use a form correctly, or if you have any doubts about its adequacy to protect you, or if what you want to do is not precisely covered by the forms provided.

EXCLUSION OF LIABILITY AND DISCLAIMER

This book is sold with the understanding that neither the authors nor the publisher is engaged in rendering legal advice. If legal advice is required, the services of a solicitor should be sought. The publisher and the authors cannot in any way guarantee that the forms in this book are being used for the purposes intended and therefore assume no responsibility for their proper and correct use.

Whilst every effort has been made to ensure that this Lawpack publication provides accurate and expert guidance, it is impossible to predict all the circumstances in which it may be used. Accordingly, neither the publisher, authors, nor any chartered certified accountants who have assisted in the production of this Lawpack publication and updated or refined it, or whose name is credited as having so assisted and updated or refined it, nor retailers, nor any other suppliers shall be liable to any person or entity with respect to any loss or damage caused or alleged to be caused as a result of the use of the information contained in or omitted from this Lawpack publication.

About *Ready-Made Company Minutes & Resolutions...*

Ready-Made Company Minutes & Resolutions contains many of the important and ready-to-complete forms and documents you need to keep proper company minutes and records.

Company record-keeping forms are at your fingertips, giving you the protection you need without the inconvenience or cost of hiring a solicitor for simple company matters you can easily handle yourself.

Lawpack's *Ready-Made Company Minutes & Resolutions* is the ideal way to 'get it in writing'. It is intended for anyone who is responsible for ensuring that the formalities of running a private company are properly observed. That includes not just the person whose title is company secretary, but also the directors and anyone else to whom they delegate the responsibility for seeing that the paperwork is in order.

The Companies Act 2006 introduced significant changes to directors' duties, notice and types of meetings, proxies, Articles of Association, written resolutions, company secretaries and company records. This book incorporates the necessary changes to the forms and documents in line with this Act and, as we understand the law requires, at the date of publication.

In *Ready-Made Company Minutes & Resolutions*, the pronoun 'he' should be read as 'he or she'.

Contents

Directors

Altering the articles of Association

SECTION A

How *Ready-Made Company Minutes & Resolutions* can help you

Why good company records are essential

No business owner has become wealthy simply by keeping good company records. But good company record keeping is essential for several important reasons.

When a company is created you create a legal entity separate and distinct from its shareholders: it has a 'separate corporate personality'. This means that the company makes contracts on its own behalf; its assets are owned by the company; and it can sue and be sued in its own name, (not the shareholders'). Because of this concept of a separate personality the directors and shareholders are, generally, not liable for the actions of the company. Directors can, however, be personally liable for things they have or have not done; for example, where they give personal guarantees or where they are guilty of wrongful or fraudulent trading, or fail to attend to certain obligatory procedures.

Normally a shareholder is liable only for the amount he has paid for his shares; for example, if he subscribes £1,000 for one thousand £1 shares and the company becomes insolvent owing millions of pounds in debts, the most he can lose is £1,000. Shareholders, like directors, can also be made liable if they are party to fraudulent trading. Even if your company has a few shareholders (or is even a single member company), the need for detailed company records is critical. Any one shareholder may challenge the authority of a decision or transaction. Only complete and accurate resolutions can verify that the action was properly authorised by the directors and/or the shareholders.

If you are a director of a company you should insist on accurate minutes of board meetings so that, if need be, you can prove your actions at these meetings and also show how you voted. Legal actions against directors are becoming more common and you must be able to defend yourself.

Forming a company

Ready-Made Company Minutes & Resolutions does not deal with setting up a limited company. This subject is covered by the Lawpack's *How to Run a Limited Company* book. However, as the Articles of Association of smaller companies often follow the standard Model Articles, a copy of this is reproduced in Appendix 2 for convenient reference. In *Ready-Made Company Minutes & Resolutions* you will also find a large selection of special resolutions which may be useful if you want to amend the articles of your company.

Running a company

The day-to-day control of a company is vested in its directors. A director may be either **executive** or **non-executive.** Generally executive directors work full-time for the company and are employed under a service agreement; non-executive directors are part-time and may have a short engagement letter describing what they are to do and how they are paid.

The board of directors will appoint certain officers, typically:

- a **chairman,** who chairs board meetings and, unless the articles say otherwise, has a casting vote; he may be executive or non-executive;
- a **managing director** or **chief executive,** who will be executive and responsible for the day- to-day management;
- a **company secretary** (not legally required after 6 April 2008, but someone has to carry out company secretarial duties and so we recommend the retention of a company secretary), who may or may not be a director and has responsibility for compliance with formalities such as filing at Companies House and keeping the company's **statutory books.**

The precise function of the officers and other directors will vary according to the company's requirements and the individuals' abilities. Executives should always have written service agreements clearly defining their role and the other terms on which they are employed; it is also desirable to record the key features of the engagement of any non-executive director.

The statutory books comprise various sections known as **registers**, e.g. of members, of directors, of directors' interests in the shares of the company and the register of charges created by the company over its assets (see specimen templates on page 155). Statutory books also include minutes of directors' and shareholders' meetings or signed resolutions. While the statutory records are usually kept at the registered office, the Companies Act does permit certain registers to be kept at other addresses within the country of incorporation, e.g. the register of members and the register of directors' interests in shares. The Registrar of Companies needs to be notified of the location of the registers. The registers need to be available for inspection for at least two hours each business day and can be inspected free of charge by any member or, on payment of the appropriate fee, by any member of the public. Auditors, if appointed, have the right to inspect the registers at any time. The registers of members, directors and secretaries will need to be checked against the pre-printed Annual Return document which is issued each year by Companies House.

Rules affecting directors

The powers of the directors are derived from the company's memorandum and articles of Association and from general company law. Their powers are extensive and it is for this reason that certain duties and restrictions are imposed on them. For example:

- a director is not allowed to make a personal profit from his position. If a director does profit from trade secrets obtained in his capacity as a director then he must account to the company for that profit.

- a director must act in accordance with the company's constitution and must only exercise powers for their proper purpose.
- a director must always act in the way he considers most likely to promote the success of the company for the benefit of all the members.
- a director must declare to the other directors the nature and extent of any direct or indirect interest he may have in any proposed transaction.
- a director must exercise independent judgement.
- a director must not exceed the power given to him; he must act in good faith in the interests of the company.
- a director owes a duty of care and skill and has to meet a certain standard dependent on his knowledge and experience.
- directors cannot pay an outgoing director a 'golden handshake' without the approval of the shareholders.
- a director cannot be granted a service contract of over two years without the approval of the shareholders.
- with certain exceptions, loans to directors are unlawful.

Conduct of board meetings

The directors exercise their power by voting collectively at board meetings or by signing written resolutions Certain formalities must be complied with in the running of board meetings; for example:

- a board meeting must be called on reasonable notice. What is reasonable depends on the subject matter of the proposed meeting. The notice does not have to be in writing.
- unless the Articles provide otherwise each director has one vote. All resolutions are passed by a majority.
- the Articles will specify a minimum number of directors who must be present in person or by their alternate in order for a meeting to be valid. Under Model Articles this 'quorum' is two, but another number may be substituted.
- minutes must be written up after every meeting and inserted into the appropriate register.

Shareholders' rights

The rights of the shareholders (or 'members') are governed by the Articles and by general law. A simple company will have just one class of shares, probably described as '**ordinary shares**'.

A more complicated structure may include '**preference shares**' or '**deferred shares**' or other designated classes with different rights.

The rights usually enjoyed by shareholders include:

a) the right to attend and vote at **General Meetings**, i.e. meetings of the shareholders;

b) the right to receive dividends if declared;

c) the right to receive a distribution of capital on a winding-up.

Typically, an ordinary shareholder has all three rights but a holder of preference shares may not have a vote or a right to participate in capital profits on a winding up. The 'preference' usually refers to a right to a fixed dividend and a fixed repayment on a winding up in priority to the ordinary shareholders.

Certain minimum percentages of voting shares are required to take particular steps of which the most important are:

% required	In order to
75	Pass a special resolution, whether written or passed at a meeting
over 50	Pass an ordinary resolution, whether written or passed at a meeting
10	Demand a poll
10	Require the board to convene a General Meeting
90	Consent to short notice

Votes at shareholders' meetings are normally cast by a show of hands when each shareholder has one vote. However, the chairman may, and if at least five[1] members or the holders of at least 10 per cent of the shares represented at the meeting so request he must, order a poll. Votes are then counted according to the numbers of shares held rather than the number of shareholders present at the meeting. Absent shareholders may appoint proxies to represent them according to the Articles. Corporate shareholders must appoint a representative to attend which is strictly not the same as a proxy and requires a slightly different form of appointment. When voting on a written resolution the same percentages as stated above apply – i.e. it's nature of the resolution that determines the majority required, not whether it's written or not.

Notice of shareholder meetings

Notice of General Meetings of shareholders must be in writing. The amount of notice depends on the type of meeting and the resolution being proposed.

Ordinary notice is required in the following cases:

General Meeting	14 clear days must be given to the members
Annual General Meeting (AGM)	14 clear days must be given to the members.
Special notice applies to:	
Any meeting where a director is being appointed	21 clear days must be given to the members
Any meeting where a director or auditor is being removed	Must leave formal written notice at registered office at least 28 days before meeting with 21 days notice given to the members.

[1] *This minimum may be lowered by the Articles, e.g. under Model Articles if at least two members demand a poll one must be held.*

It is possible to call a meeting on short notice. For any General Meeting, members holding at least 90 per cent of all the shares must agree.

For a resolution to be validly passed the meeting must be quorate, i.e. a minimum number ('quorum') of members must be present to make the meeting valid. As mentioned above, under Model Articles the requirement is two; this can be increased if the Articles are altered. It cannot generally be decreased unless it is a one-member company.

Minutes must be written up and signed by the chairman after every meeting.

How to use *Ready-Made Company Minutes & Resolutions...*

Using Lawpack's *Ready-Made Company Minutes & Resolutions* is straightforward. Follow the steps below.

Note that the material in *Ready-Made Company Minutes & Resolutions* can be used by any private company of any size. It is not suitable for public limited companies, those listed on the Stock Exchange or those limited by guarantee.

1. Decisions on the running of a company are made by passing resolutions. When questions arise for decision, ask yourself if it is a matter for the directors. If so, do they require a meeting? If yes, go to **section B** which contains standard forms for minutes and examples to show you how they are to be completed.

2. If instead they are agreed that it is simply a matter of signing a written resolution, go to **section C**. The forms for written board resolutions are set out in full in this section; you may wish to combine two or more resolutions from these forms when there is more than one matter to be decided.

3. Alternatively, if the decision is one for the shareholders, does it require a special resolution or an ordinary resolution; and can it dealt with by a signed resolution or is a meeting required? If a meeting is required, go to **section D** where you will find the form of notice to be sent to shareholders, minutes and a number of other forms which may be relevant. If, on the other hand, the written resolution procedure may be used, go to **section E** where you will find example resolutions contained in an appropriate form and on page 99 detailed instructions on their use. When meetings are needed, you should pay careful attention to the requirements for notice, a quorum at the meeting and voting. In the case of written resolutions, notice and quorum do not apply but you must obtain all the necessary signatures and the resolution is not valid until this has been done.

4. Consult the contents pages of *Ready-Made Company Minutes & Resolutions* to see which resolutions can be passed by directors and those which have to be passed by members as special or ordinary resolutions. *Ready-Made Company Minutes & Resolutions* resolutions have been drafted as directors' written resolutions or standard written resolutions of members, i.e. drafted for use without meetings having to be held by the board or by members. If required, the actual resolution wording can be inserted into the Standard Minutes of Board Meetings or of Members' Meetings.

5. Cut out and photocopy the form you want and keep the original so it can be used again in the future. Alternatively, for convenience you can download Microsoft Word versions of all the documents – see panel opposite for instructions.

6. Complete each form fully. Make certain all blanks (name, address, dates, amounts, etc.) are filled in. You may need to delete or add provisions in some forms to suit your requirements. If this is necessary, make sure each deletion or insertion is initialled by all parties.

7. Some forms have footnotes which should be observed if you are to use the form properly. Some forms refer to others in *Ready-Made Company Minutes & Resolutions*, copies of documents which will need to be attached to the form before use or Companies House forms available from Companies House at the following address:

   Companies House
   Crown Way
   Cardiff CF4 3UZ

   Tel. 0303 1234 500
   www.gov.uk/government/organisations/companies-house

8. It is important that the company submits accounts and annual returns to Companies House when they become due. Failure to submit these documents can result in the Registrar of Companies commencing action to have the company dissolved. If the company is dissolved, all assets fall to the Crown and the restoration process can be time-consuming and expensive. Should accounts be submitted late to Companies House, late filing penalties are automatically imposed on the company; this penalty is in addition to any penalties that could be imposed on the directors personally.

9. The aim of *Ready-Made Company Minutes & Resolutions* is that it be as simple to follow as possible. That means it cannot deal with every set of circumstances which may arise or list every step you may need to take to comply with company law. If you have any doubt about what to do, you should always take professional advice from the company's lawyers or accountants.

DOWNLOADABLE DOCUMENTS

For convenience and ease of use, all the documents in *Ready-Made Company Minutes & Resolutions* are available to download and use in Microsoft Word format.

To access your documents all you need to do is:

1. Enter **www.lawpack.co.uk/B616** in your browser's address bar,
2. Under the heading **Downloads** enter the code printed below into the registration box.

   REGISTRATION CODE: **B6161508051**

3. Click the **Activate!** button to access your downloads

Terms and conditions apply. Please check www.lawpack.co.uk/terms.asp for more information

Company decision-making process

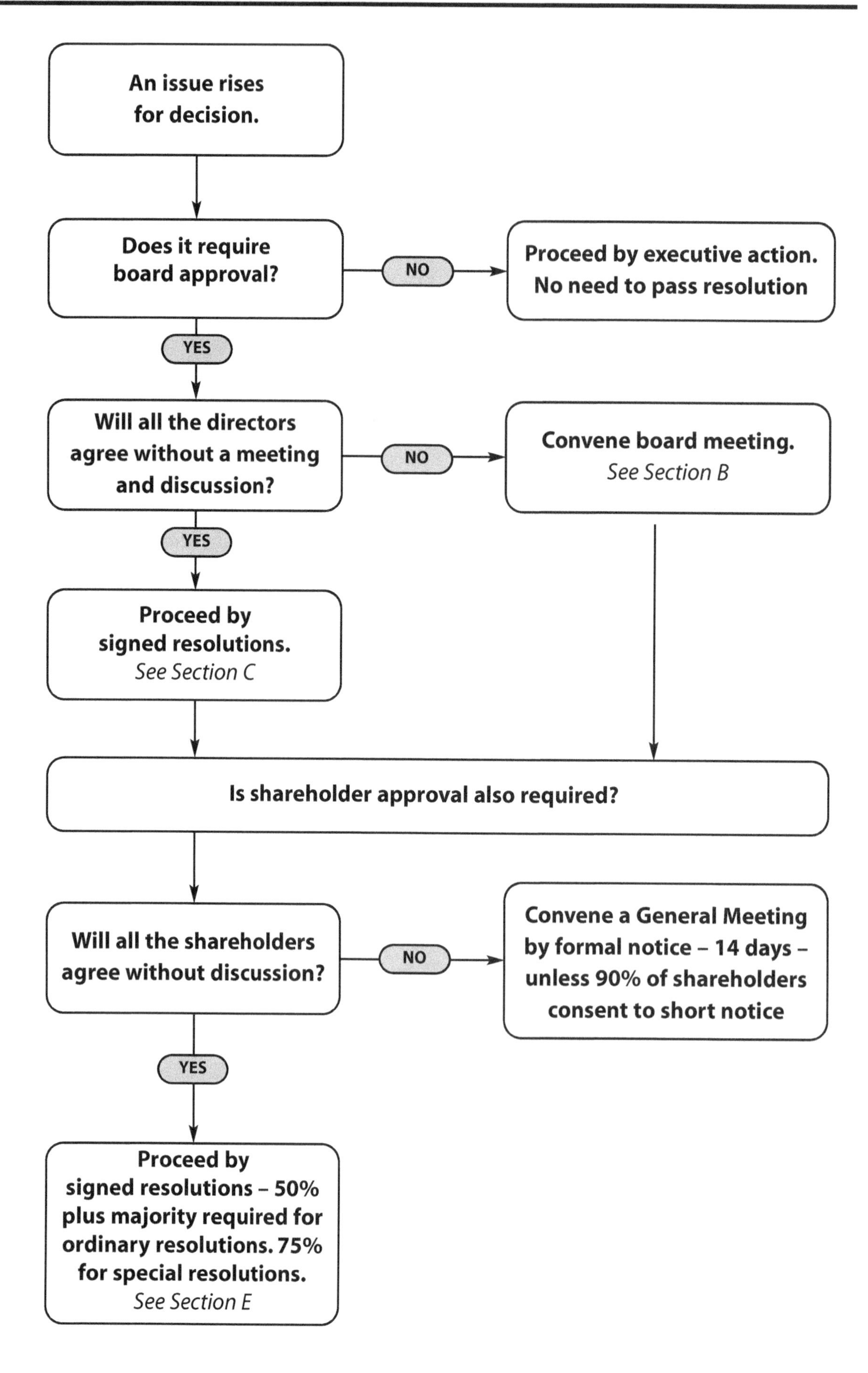

SECTION B

Board Meetings

When an issue arises for decision relating to a company, first ask yourself whether it requires board approval. It is beyond the scope of *Ready Made Company Minutes and Resolutions* to provide an exhaustive list of such issues; but some examples are: the approval of important contracts to be entered into, the approval of transfers of shares in the company, the allotment of shares (although the directors must have the necessary authority to do this), the approval of the company's accounts and the changing of the company's registered office. If you decide that a board resolution is required but all the directors will agree without discussion, proceed by written resolution - see Section C onwards. However, if you need a board resolution but it also requires a meeting to discuss the issue, use the forms in this section. In addition, certain matters will require the approval of the company's shareholders in which case the directors should pass a resolution calling a general meeting or proposing a written resolution to deal with the issue in question (examples of these kinds of resolutions are also included in Section C). The text of the actual resolution you require can be selected from those in Section C and then be inserted into the board minutes as appropriate. Where a document is referred to as being attached to the written resolution this should be replaced in the resolution in minute form by reference to the relevant document being 'produced at the meeting'.

Steps to be taken for holding board meetings:

1. Give all the directors proper notice of the meeting. There is no fixed period and in an emergency a meeting may be convened at once but generally allow as much time as is reasonably possible. The Model Articles provide that it is not necessary to give notice of a meeting to a director who is absent from the United Kingdom; if a director is, for any reason, resident abroad, consideration should be given to amending the Articles of Association.
2. When the meeting begins, ensure that a quorum is present.
3. When the meeting is concluded, prepare minutes, circulate them for comments and once approved have them signed by the chairman and filed in the minute book.
4. Consider whether any matter requires to be notified to Companies House or the auditors and, if so, attend to it. Notes on the forms will assist in identifying when this is necessary but they should not be taken to be exhaustive.

B01 **Notice of board meeting**—Announces to all company directors the time, place and agenda of an upcoming board meeting.

B02 **Notice of appointment of alternate director**—to be given to the secretary by a director who appoints an alternate. A form of resolution approving the appointment is at C11. An alternate may require board approval under the Articles and cannot attend meetings until notice of the appointment has been given. A director may attend meetings himself instead of an alternate.

B03 **Minutes of First Board Meeting**—a number of routine matters must be attended to at the first meeting of directors following incorporation.

B04 **Example Minutes of First Board Meeting**—for guidance when completing form B03, typical details have been inserted in this example.

B05 **Standard board minutes**—all minutes of board meetings must set out the date, time and place of the meeting and who has attended. Those who are directors are shown as 'present' and anyone else as 'in attendance'. Select the resolutions you require from those set out in Section C.

B06 **Example Board Minutes**—to illustrate how to use Form B05, typical details have been inserted in this example

Notice of Board Meeting Form B01

_______________ LIMITED

Notice is hereby given[1] that a meeting of the directors of the company will be held at _______________ on _______________ at ______ a.m./p.m. at which your attendance is requested.

AGENDA

1. Apologies for absence

2. Approval of minutes of last board meeting held on _______________.

3. _______________

4. _______________

Signed: _______________ Dated:

[1] *Must be called on reasonable notice*

Notice of Appointment of Alternate Director — Form B02

________________________ LIMITED

THE DIRECTORS

____

____

____

____

I hereby give notice that I have appointed ________________________________

of ____

____

to be my alternate director. I hereby request that the board approves this appointment.[1]

Signed: ________________________________ Dated: ________________

[1] *Check Articles to ensure that an alternate can be appointed; regulations 65 to 69 of Table A and Section 5 of the Model Articles permit the appointment of alternate directors. The appointment may not require board approval. The appointment can be revoked at any time by the appointing director.*

Minutes of First Board Meeting — Form B03

______________________ **LIMITED**

MINUTES of the first Meeting of the Board of Directors held at
______________________ on ________________ at ______ a.m./p.m.

PRESENT:

____

____

____

IN ATTENDANCE:

____

____

____

____

1. The Chairman confirmed that notice of the meeting had been given to all the directors of the Company and that a quorum of the board of directors was present at the meeting.
2. The Chairman reported that the Company had been incorporated on ______________________ and produced the certificate of incorporation and a print of the Memorandum and Articles of Association of the Company as filed at the Companies Registry.
3. It was noted that the first Directors of the Company are ____________________

   ____

   ____

   ____

   and its first Secretary is ______________________________.
4. It was further noted that the registered office of the Company was situated at ________________________.
5. IT WAS RESOLVED that ____________________ be appointed auditors to the Company to act as such until the conclusion of the first annual general meeting of the Company and that their remuneration be at a rate to be subsequently agreed.
6. IT WAS RESOLVED that the accounts of the Company be made up to ______________ each year.[1]

[1] *This is the company's annual accounting reference date. It is set automatically on the last day of the month in which the anniversary of the company's incorporation falls. This resolution is therefore only needed if the directors wish to change this date. A company's first accounting reference date can be up to 18 months from the date of incorporation.*
If a company qualifies as 'small', has a turnover of less than £6.5 million (for financial periods starting on or after 6 April 2008) and a balance sheet total (for financial periods starting on or after 6 April 2008) of not more than £3.26 million, it can, subject to fulfilling certain other conditions, be exempt from the obligation to appoint auditors.

Minutes of First Board Meeting (cont) — Form B03

7. IT WAS RESOLVED that ______________ Bank Plc, ______________________ branch be appointed bankers of the Company and that the resolutions set out on the form of mandate produced to the meeting (a copy of which is annexed hereto) be approved and passed and deemed to be set out herein in extenso.
8. IT WAS RESOLVED that the seal produced to the meeting, an impression of which is affixed to these Minutes, be approved and adopted as the common seal of the Company and that it be kept in safe custody by the Secretary.] [2]
9. The Chairman reported the receipt of the sum of £2 representing payment in full for the shares subscribed for by the subscribers to the Memorandum of Association. [It was noted that the subscribers had waived their rights to share certificates.][3] IT WAS RESOLVED that the names of the subscribers be entered in the register of members in respect of such shares.
10. There were produced to and considered by the meeting the following transfers of shares [with supporting certificates]:

    Transferor: ____________ Transferee: ____________ No. of shares: ____________

    Transferor: ____________ Transferee: ____________ No. of shares: ____________
11. IT WAS RESOLVED that:
    a. subject to their being represented duly stamped, such transfers be approved;
    b. the names of the transferees be entered in the register of members in respect of the shares transferred to them; and
    c. the Secretary be instructed to prepare share certificates in respect of the shares transferred and to deliver them to the transferees.
12. The Secretary was instructed to arrange for a nameplate to be ordered and affixed outside the registered office.
13. The Secretary was instructed to file Form AA01 (accounting reference date) with the registrar of companies.[4]
14. IT WAS RESOLVED that the Company should trade under the name ____.

    The Secretary was instructed to ensure compliance with the statutory disclosure requirements in the Business Names Act 1985.
15. The payment of the fees incurred in respect of the formation of the company was approved.
16. The Secretary was instructed to register the company with HM Customs & Excise for the purposes of VAT and to supply particulars to the Inland Revenue for tax purposes.
17. There being no other business the meeting ended.

Chairman: ____

[2] *A seal is no longer a requirement.*

[3] *Include only where the subscribers are to transfer their shares immediately; if shares are nil or partly paid they should be numbered.*

[4] *Include only if accounting reference date has been changed.*

Example Minutes of First Board Meeting — Form B04

Lawpack Publishing **LIMITED**

MINUTES of the first Meeting of the Board of Directors held at
2 James Road, London SE1 on 2nd Sept 2015 at 10.00 a.m./~~p.m~~.

PRESENT:
James Etheridge (in the chair)
Peggy Flanagan
Russell Coles

IN ATTENDANCE:
Caroline Dore

1. The Chairman confirmed that notice of the meeting had been given to all the directors of the Company and that a quorum of the board of directors was present at the meeting.
2. The Chairman reported that the Company had been incorporated on Wednesday 27th July 2015 and produced the certificate of incorporation and a print of the Memorandum and Articles of Association of the Company as filed at the Companies Registry.
3. It was noted that the first Directors of the Company are
James Etheridge (in the chair)
Peggy Flanagan
Russell Coles
and its first Secretary is James Etheridge.
4. It was further noted that the registered office of the Company was situated at 2 James Road, London SE1.
5. IT WAS RESOLVED that John Ross & Company be appointed auditors to the Company to act as such until the conclusion of the first annual general meeting of the Company and that their remuneration be at a rate to be subsequently agreed.
6. IT WAS RESOLVED that the accounts of the Company be made up to 31st March each year.

Example Minutes of First Board Meeting (cont) Form B04

7. IT WAS RESOLVED that *Westminster* Bank Plc, *Southwark* branch be appointed bankers of the Company and that the resolutions set out on the form of mandate produced to the meeting (a copy of which is annexed hereto) be approved and passed and deemed to be set out herein in extenso.
8. IT WAS RESOLVED that the seal produced to the meeting, an impression of which is affixed to these Minutes, be approved and adopted as the common seal of the Company and that it be kept in safe custody by the Secretary.]
9. The Chairman reported the receipt of the sum of £2 representing payment in full for the shares subscribed for by the subscribers to the Memorandum of Association. [It was noted that the subscribers had waived their rights to share certificates.] IT WAS RESOLVED that the names of the subscribers be entered in the register of members in respect of such shares.
10. There were produced to and considered by the meeting the following transfers of shares [with supporting certificates]:
    Transferor: *John Doe* Transferee: *James Etheridge* No. of shares: *1*
    Transferor: *Joy Stag* Transferee: *Penny Flanagan* No. of shares: *1*
11. IT WAS RESOLVED that:
    a. subject to their being represented duly stamped, such transfers be approved;
    b. the names of the transferees be entered in the register of members in respect of the shares transferred to them; and
    c. the Secretary be instructed to prepare share certificates in respect of the shares transferred and to deliver them to the transferees.
12. The Secretary was instructed to arrange for a nameplate to be ordered and affixed outside the registered office.
13. The Secretary was instructed to file Form AA01 (accounting reference date) with the registrar of companies.
14. IT WAS RESOLVED that the Company should trade under the name *Take Note*.
    The Secretary was instructed to ensure compliance with the statutory disclosure requirements in the Business Names Act 1985.
15. The payment of the fees incurred in respect of the formation of the company was approved.
16. The Secretary was instructed to register the company with HM Customs & Excise for the purposes of VAT and to supply particulars to the Inland Revenue for tax purposes.
17. There being no other business the meeting ended.

Chairman: *J. Etheridge*

Standard Board Minutes — Form B05

________________________ LIMITED

MINUTES of a Meeting of the Board of Directors held at ________________________
on ________________________ at __________________ a.m./p.m.

PRESENT:

____(in the chair)

____

____

____

IN ATTENDANCE:

____

____

____

____

The Chairman confirmed that notice of the meeting had been given to all the directors of the Company and that a quorum of the board of directors was present at the meeting.

____________________ declared his/their interest(s) in the following contract(s) which were discussed at the meeting ____.

IT WAS RESOLVED THAT

____

____

____

____

There being no further business the meeting then ended.

Chairman: ____

[1] *A director is under a duty to declare any interest he may have, whether direct or indirect in a contract or proposed contract with the company at the first meeting at which the question of entering into the contract is considered. If he becomes interested subsequently he must declare his interest at the next board meeting.*

Example Standard Board Minutes — Form B06

Lawpack Publishing **LIMITED**

MINUTES of a Meeting of the Board of Directors held at 2 James Road, London SE1 on 2nd Sept 2015 at 10.00 a.m./~~p.m.~~

PRESENT:

James Etheridge (in the chair)

Peggy Flanagan

Russell Coles

IN ATTENDANCE:

Caroline Dore

The Chairman confirmed that notice of the meeting had been given to all the directors of the Company and that a quorum of the board of directors was present at the meeting.

James Etheridge declared his/their interest(s) in the following contract(s) which were to be discussed at the meeting: supply of paper from XYZ Paper, P/O 1234567.

IT WAS RESOLVED THAT

Russell Coles shall cease to be secretary of the Company with effect from 30th September 2015

There being no further business the meeting then ended.

Chairman: James Etheridge

SECTION C

Board Resolutions

The forms in this section are designed to be used as written resolutions without holding a board meeting (although the text of the resolutions themselves may be inserted into the minutes of a board meeting, as described in Section B). In order to avoid a meeting it is necessary that:

- the Articles of Association allow board resolutions which are signed by the directors;
- the resolution is signed by all the directors entitled to receive notice of a meeting of directors;
- the resolution is dated with the date on which it is signed by the last of the directors to sign and is then placed in the company's Minute Book.

If the above conditions are not satisfied, it will be necessary to hold a meeting; see Section B.

Although written resolutions must be signed by every director, they may sign separate copies and the resolutions will then be effective when the last one signs and sends it back to the secretary; a fax may be sent, but the original must also be sent afterwards.

Appointment and removal of officers

C01 **Appointment of director**—Resolves to appoint a director.

C02 **Proposal to remove director**—Resolves to hold a General Meeting to propose removing a director.

C03 **Appointment of chairman**—Resolves to appoint a chairman.

C04 **Removal of chairman**—Resolves to remove existing chairman.

C05 **Appointment of secretary**—Resolves to appoint a secretary.

C06 **Removal of secretary**—Resolves to remove existing secretary.

C07 **Appointment of auditors**—Resolves to appoint auditors.

C08 **Proposal to remove auditors**—Resolves to hold a General Meeting to propose removing auditors.

C09 **Notice to auditors of proposed removal**—Notifies auditors of a General Meeting to propose their removal

C10 **Appointment of bankers**—Resolves to appoint bankers.

Directors

C11 Approval of alternate director—Resolves to approve an alternate director.

C12 Proposal of variation of maximum number of directors—Resolves to hold a General Meeting to propose limiting the number of directors the company may have.

C13 Proposal of compensation payment—Resolves to hold a General Meeting to propose giving compensation payment to a resigning board member.

C14 Approval of directors' report and accounts—Resolves to approve the directors' report and annual accounts.

C15 Approval of director's service contract—Resolves to approve a director's service contract with the company for less than five years.

C16 Proposal of approval of director's service contract of more than two years' duration—Resolves to hold a General Meeting to propose signing a director's service contract of more than two years.

C17 Proposal of director's remuneration—Resolves to hold a General Meeting to propose paying a director a designated amount.

C18 Proposal to allow director to vote on contracts where there is a personal interest—Resolves to hold a General Meeting to propose approving of a director voting on contracts with a company of which he is a director or shareholder.

C19 Proposal that members ratify acts of directors beyond the powers delegated to them—Resolves to hold a General Meeting to propose ratifying acts of the board of directors which were beyond the powers delegated to them.

Shares

C20 Proposal of bonus issue—Resolves to hold a General Meeting to propose issuing shares by way of a bonus.

C21 Allotment of shares—Resolves to allot shares to an applicant.

C22 Proposal of dividend—Resolves to hold a General Meeting to propose paying a dividend to shareholders.

C23 Proposal of purchase of own shares—Resolves to hold a General Meeting to propose the company's purchase of its own shares from a shareholder.

C24 Proposal of purchase of own shares from capital—Resolves to hold a General Meeting to propose the company's purchase of its own shares funded from its capital.

C25 Approval and registration of transfer of shares—Approves the transfer of shares from a shareholder to someone else and resolves to register those shares in that person's name.

C26 Proposal that directors be given authority to make a specific allotment of shares for a specified purpose—Resolves to hold a General Meeting to propose granting directors the authority to make a specific allotment of shares for a specified purpose.

C27 Proposal that directors be given authority to allot shares generally—Resolves to hold a General Meeting to propose granting directors a general authority to allot shares for a period of up to five years or, if the relevant elective resolution is in place, for an indefinite period.

C28 Proposal of revocation of directors' authority to allot shares —Resolves to hold a General Meeting to propose taking away authority previously given to the directors to allot shares.

C29 Proposal of removal of statutory pre-emption rights —Resolves to hold a General Meeting to propose the removal of the statutory rights of existing shareholders to be offered any shares which are to be allotted before they are allotted to anyone else.

Constitution

C30 Proposal of alteration of Articles—Resolves to hold a General Meeting to propose changing the Articles of Association.

C31 Proposal of alteration of objects—Resolves to hold a General Meeting to propose changing the objects of the company as they are set out in the Memorandum of Association.

C32 Proposal of alteration of Articles - no retirement by rotation—Resolves to hold a General Meeting to propose changing the Articles so that directors do not have to retire by rotation.

C33 Proposal of alteration of Articles - removal of chairman's casting vote—Resolves to hold a General Meeting to propose changing the Articles so that the chairman shall not have a casting vote.

C34 Proposal of alteration of Articles - director voting where personal interest—Resolves to hold a General Meeting to propose changing the Articles so that the chairman shall not have a casting vote.

C35 Proposal of alteration of Articles - refusal to register transfer of shares—Resolves to hold a General Meeting to change the Articles so that directors do not have register the transfer of a share.

C36 Proposal of alteration of Articles - quorum for General Meeting—Resolves to hold a General Meeting to change the Articles so that if a quorum is not present at a General Meeting the meeting be adjourned.

C37 Proposal of alteration of Articles - number of directors—Resolves to hold a General Meeting to change the Articles so that number of directors may be varied.

C38 Proposal of alteration of Articles - alternate directors—Resolves to hold a General Meeting to propose changing the Articles so that directors may specify that a proportion of their remuneration is paid to their alternate.

C39 Proposal of alteration of Articles - weighted voting rights—Resolves to hold a General Meeting to change the Articles so that voting rights of directors are weighted according to number of shares held, in order to prevent the directors from being removed from office.

C40 Proposal of alteration of Articles - authority to allot shares—Resolves to hold a General Meeting to change the Articles so that directors have authority to allot shares.

C41 Proposal of adoption of new Articles—Resolves to hold a General Meeting to propose adopting new Articles of Association.

C42 Proposal of name change—Resolves to hold a General Meeting to propose changing the name of the company.

C43 Adoption of trading name—Resolves to adopt a trading name.

C44 Proposal that company re-register as a Public Limited Company—Resolves to hold a General Meeting to propose re-registering as a public limited company.

C45 Change address of registered office—Resolves to change the address of the registered office.

C46 Adoption of company seal—Resolves to adopt a company seal.

Financial

C47 Change of accounting reference date—Resolves to change the date on which the company's financial year ends.

C48 Proposal of voluntary liquidation where company insolvent—Resolves to hold a General Meeting to propose beginning to wind up because the company is insolvent and cannot pay its debts.

C49 Proposal of voluntary liquidation where company solvent—Resolves to hold a General Meeting to propose the winding up of the company.

C50 Application for an administration order—Resolves to apply for an administrator to be appointed to run the company while it is unable to pay its debts.

C51 Approval of auditors' remuneration for audit—Resolves to pay the auditors a fee for auditing the annual financial records.

C52 Approval of auditors' remuneration for services and advice—Resolves to pay the company's auditors a fee for their services and advice.

C53 Registration for VAT—Resolves to register for value added tax. Registration is obligatory if value of taxable supplies in the past 12 months or less has exceeded £64,000.

C54 Issue of debenture—Resolves to give the directors authority to issue a document stating the terms of a loan.

C55 Proposal of approval of substantial property transaction—Resolves to hold a General Meeting to approve a substantial property transaction involving a director of the company.

Appointment of Director — Form C01

Company Number: ________________

THE COMPANIES ACT
PRIVATE COMPANY LIMITED BY SHARES
WRITTEN RESOLUTION OF THE BOARD OF DIRECTORS

______________________ LIMITED

Pursuant to the Articles of Association of the company the undersigned, being all the directors of the company, hereby resolve:

THAT ________________________________, having indicated his/her willingness to act, be appointed as a director of the Company with effect from ______________________.[1]

Directors' signatures:	Date of each signature:
________________________	________________________
________________________	________________________
________________________	________________________

[1] *Companies House Form AP01 (or AP02 for a corporate director) to be completed and submitted to Companies House within 14 days of appointment; the register of directors should be updated.*

All directors must sign a written resolution.

Proposal to Remove Director

Form C02

Company Number: ______________

THE COMPANIES ACT
PRIVATE COMPANY LIMITED BY SHARES
WRITTEN RESOLUTION OF THE BOARD OF DIRECTORS

______________________ LIMITED

Pursuant to the Articles of Association of the company, the undersigned, being all the directors of the company, hereby resolve:

THAT a General Meeting be convened to propose the removal of ________________ as director with effect from ______________________________________.[1]

Directors' signatures:	Date of each signature:
______________________________	______________________________
______________________________	______________________________
______________________________	______________________________

[1] A member must give special notice of this resolution i.e. must leave formal notice at the registered office at least 28 days before the General Meeting. The company must inform the director concerned (see Forms D09-D11). The written resolution procedure cannot be used.

All directors must sign a written resolution.

Appointment of Chairman Form C03

Company Number: ________________

THE COMPANIES ACT
PRIVATE COMPANY LIMITED BY SHARES
WRITTEN RESOLUTION OF THE BOARD OF DIRECTORS

_____________________________ LIMITED

Pursuant to the Articles of Association of the company the undersigned, being all the directors of the company, hereby resolve:

THAT ____ , be appointed as chairman of the Company with effect from ____.

Directors' signatures:	Date of each signature:
____________________________________	____________________________________
____________________________________	____________________________________
____________________________________	____________________________________

All directors must sign a written resolution.

Removal of Chairman — Form C04

Company Number: ______________

THE COMPANIES ACT
PRIVATE COMPANY LIMITED BY SHARES
WRITTEN RESOLUTION OF THE BOARD OF DIRECTORS

______________________ LIMITED

Pursuant to the Articles of Association of the company, the undersigned, being all the directors of the company, hereby resolve:

THAT ____, shall cease to be chairman of the Company with effect from ____.

Directors' signatures:	Date of each signature:
______________________________	______________________________
______________________________	______________________________
______________________________	______________________________

All directors must sign a written resolution.

Appointment of Secretary — Form C05

Company Number: ______________

THE COMPANIES ACT
PRIVATE COMPANY LIMITED BY SHARES
WRITTEN RESOLUTION OF THE BOARD OF DIRECTORS

________________________ LIMITED

Pursuant to the Articles of Association of the company, the undersigned, being all the directors of the company, hereby resolve:

THAT ______________________________, having indicated his/her willingness to act, be appointed as secretary of the Company with effect from ____________________.[1]

Directors' signatures:	Date of each signature:
______________________________	______________________________
______________________________	______________________________
______________________________	______________________________

[1] File Companies House form AP03 (or AP04 for a corporate secretary).

All directors must sign a written resolution.

Removal of Secretary — Form C06

Company Number: ________________

THE COMPANIES ACT
PRIVATE COMPANY LIMITED BY SHARES
WRITTEN RESOLUTION OF THE BOARD OF DIRECTORS

________________________ LIMITED

Pursuant to the Articles of Association of the company, the undersigned, being all the directors of the company, hereby resolve:

THAT ____, shall cease to be secretary of the Company with effect from ____.[1]

Directors' signatures:	Date of each signature:
______________________________	______________________________
______________________________	______________________________
______________________________	______________________________

[1] *File Companies House form TM02.*

All directors must sign a written resolution.

Appointment of Auditors — Form C07

Company Number: ______________

THE COMPANIES ACT
PRIVATE COMPANY LIMITED BY SHARES
WRITTEN RESOLUTION OF THE BOARD OF DIRECTORS

______________________ LIMITED

Pursuant to the Articles of Association of the company, the undersigned, being all the directors of the company, hereby resolve:

THAT ____
of ____ be the auditors
of the Company with effect from ______________________ at a fee to be agreed.[1]

Directors' signatures: Date of each signature:

______________________ ______________________

______________________ ______________________

______________________ ______________________

[1] *Generally, the directors may appoint only the first auditors of the company who may hold office until the conclusion of the first General Meeting at which accounts are presented to the members. The auditors must then be reappointed at this General Meeting or, subject to the giving of special notice, an alternative auditor can be appointed by a resolution of the shareholders. The directors may also, however, fill any casual vacancy in the office of auditor – such appointment is only effective until the conclusion of the next General Meeting at which accounts are presented to the shareholders.*

All directors must sign a written resolution.

Proposal to Remove Auditors — Form C08

Company Number: ______________

THE COMPANIES ACT
PRIVATE COMPANY LIMITED BY SHARES
WRITTEN RESOLUTION OF THE BOARD OF DIRECTORS

______________________ LIMITED

Pursuant to the Articles of Association of the company, the undersigned, being all the directors of the company, hereby resolve:[1]

THAT a General Meeting be held at ______________________________________
on ________________________________ at __________ am/pm to propose
the removal of Messrs ______________________________________ as auditors
of the Company with effect from ________________________________.[2]

Directors' signatures:	Date of each signature:
______________________________	______________________________
______________________________	______________________________
______________________________	______________________________

[1] *This resolution is to be used where the auditors are to be removed before their term of office has expired.*

[2] *Notice must be given to the auditors,* *see Form C09.*

Notice to Auditors of Proposed Removal — Form C09

_______________ LIMITED

Dear Sirs

This letter[1] is to give you formal notice that the enclosed special notice of a resolution that you be removed as the company's auditors has been received by the company. The directors have resolved to convene a General Meeting for the purpose of considering, and if thought fit, passing this resolution.

In accordance with the Companies Act 2006 you are entitled to make representations in writing in respect of this resolution and to have them circulated to all the members of the company. If you wish to make any representations to the company, please send them to me, in writing, by _______________.[2]

Yours faithfully

____

Director/Secretary

[1] Send as soon as special notice is received. Enclose a copy of the special notice.

[2] Insert date on which Notice of General Meeting is to be sent to shareholders.

All directors must sign a written resolution.

Appointment of Bankers — Form C10

Company Number: ______________

THE COMPANIES ACT
PRIVATE COMPANY LIMITED BY SHARES
WRITTEN RESOLUTION OF THE BOARD OF DIRECTORS

______________________ LIMITED

Pursuant to the Articles of Association of the company, the undersigned, being all the directors of the company, hereby resolve:

THAT ____
of ____ be appointed as the bankers of the Company, that the resolutions contained in the Bank's formal mandate annexed hereto be approved and deemed to be set out in this resolution in extenso and that the signatories named therein be authorised to sign the same as appropriate.[1]

Directors' signatures:	Date of each signature:
____________________	____________________
____________________	____________________
____________________	____________________

[1] *Attach copy of bank's formal mandate*

All directors must sign a written resolution.

Approval of Alternate Director — Form C11

Company Number: ______________

THE COMPANIES ACT
PRIVATE COMPANY LIMITED BY SHARES
WRITTEN RESOLUTION OF THE BOARD OF DIRECTORS

______________________ LIMITED

Pursuant to the Articles of Association of the company, the undersigned, being all the directors of the company, hereby resolve:

THAT the appointment of ____ , having indicated his/her willingness to act, as alternate director for ______ be approved.[1]

Directors' signatures:	Date of each signature:
______________________	______________________
______________________	______________________
______________________	______________________

[1] *File Companies House form AP01 (or AP02 for a corporate director) in respect of appointment of alternate director. Update the registers of directors and, if appropriate, the register of directors' interests in the shares (if appropriate).*

All directors must sign a written resolution.

Proposal of Variation of Maximum Number of Directors — Form C12

Company Number: ______________

THE COMPANIES ACT
PRIVATE COMPANY LIMITED BY SHARES
WRITTEN RESOLUTION OF THE BOARD OF DIRECTORS

______________________ LIMITED

Pursuant to the Articles of Association of the company, the undersigned, being all the directors of the company, hereby resolve:

THAT a General Meeting be convened to propose that the maximum number of directors be fixed at ____
and that the company's Articles of Association be amended accordingly.

Directors' signatures:	Date of each signature:
______________________	______________________
______________________	______________________
______________________	______________________

All directors must sign a written resolution.

Proposal of Compensation Payment Form C13

Company Number: ________________

THE COMPANIES ACT
PRIVATE COMPANY LIMITED BY SHARES
WRITTEN RESOLUTION OF THE BOARD OF DIRECTORS

____________________________ LIMITED

Pursuant to the Articles of Association of the company, the undersigned, being all the directors of the company, hereby resolve:

THAT a General Meeting be convened to propose that compensation of________________
be paid to ____
on his resignation from the Board.

Directors' signatures:	Date of each signature:
____________________________________	____________________________________
____________________________________	____________________________________
____________________________________	____________________________________

All directors must sign a written resolution.

Approval of Directors' Report and Accounts — Form C14

Company Number: ______________

THE COMPANIES ACT
PRIVATE COMPANY LIMITED BY SHARES
WRITTEN RESOLUTION OF THE BOARD OF DIRECTORS

______________________ LIMITED

Pursuant to the Articles of Association of the company, the undersigned, being all the directors of the company, hereby resolve:

THAT the directors' report and accounts for the year ended ______________________
have been prepared in accordance with the Companies Act 2006 and are hereby approved, and ____
be authorised to sign the report and the balance sheet on behalf of the company.

Directors' signatures:	Date of each signature:
______________________________	______________________________
______________________________	______________________________
______________________________	______________________________

All directors must sign a written resolution.

Approval of Director's Service Contract — Form C15

Company Number: ______________

THE COMPANIES ACT
PRIVATE COMPANY LIMITED BY SHARES
WRITTEN RESOLUTION OF THE BOARD OF DIRECTORS

______________________ LIMITED

Pursuant to the Articles of Association of the company, the undersigned, being all the directors of the company and having formally declared their interests in the matter hereby resolve to approve the terms of the proposed service contract between the Company and ____
in the terms set out in the copy annexed hereto.[1]

Directors' signatures: Date of each signature:

Directors' signatures	Date of each signature
______________________	______________________
______________________	______________________
______________________	______________________

[1] *If service contracts are for a fixed term over two years, the members must approve the terms by an ordinary resolution in a General Meeting.*

All directors must sign a written resolution.

Proposal of Approval of Director's Service Contract of more than Two Years' Duration

Form C16

Company Number: ______________

THE COMPANIES ACT
PRIVATE COMPANY LIMITED BY SHARES
WRITTEN RESOLUTION OF THE BOARD OF DIRECTORS

______________________ LIMITED

Pursuant to the Articles of Association of the company and the directors having formally declared their interests in the matter, the undersigned, being all directors of the company hereby resolve:

THAT a General Meeting be convened to propose that ______________________ be awarded a service contract in excess of two years on the terms annexed hereto and hereby approved by the directors.

Directors' signatures:	Date of each signature:
______________________	______________________
______________________	______________________
______________________	______________________

All directors must sign a written resolution.

Proposal of Director's Remuneration — Form C17

Company Number: ______________

THE COMPANIES ACT
PRIVATE COMPANY LIMITED BY SHARES
WRITTEN RESOLUTION OF THE BOARD OF DIRECTORS

______________________ LIMITED

Pursuant to the Articles of Association of the company, the undersigned, being all the directors of the company, hereby resolve:

THAT a General Meeting be convened to propose that the payment of £ ____________
be paid to ____
as remuneration on a ______________________________________ basis.

Directors' signatures:	Date of each signature:
______________________	______________________
______________________	______________________
______________________	______________________

All directors must sign a written resolution.

Proposal to Allow Director to Vote on Contracts where he has a Personal Interest

Form C18

Company Number: ______________

THE COMPANIES ACT
PRIVATE COMPANY LIMITED BY SHARES
WRITTEN RESOLUTION OF THE BOARD OF DIRECTORS

______________________ LIMITED

Pursuant to the Articles of Association of the company, the undersigned, being all the directors of the company, hereby resolve:

THAT a General Meeting be convened to propose that, _________________who is a director of this company, may vote on contracts between this company and ___________ notwithstanding that he has declared his interest as a director/shareholder of ____.

Directors' signatures:	Date of each signature:
______________________	______________________
______________________	______________________
______________________	______________________

All directors must sign a written resolution.

Proposal that Members Ratify Acts of Directors Beyond the Powers Delegated to Them

Form C19

Company Number: ______________

THE COMPANIES ACT
PRIVATE COMPANY LIMITED BY SHARES
WRITTEN RESOLUTION OF THE BOARD OF DIRECTORS

______________________ LIMITED

Pursuant to the Articles of Association of the company, the undersigned, being all the directors of the company, hereby resolve:

THAT a General Meeting be convened to propose that all acts of the directors done prior to the date of this resolution be confirmed and ratified notwithstanding any matter that might otherwise cause their validity to be in doubt.[1]

Directors' signatures:	Date of each signature:
______________________	______________________
______________________	______________________
______________________	______________________

[1] Where the board of directors act beyond the powers delegated to them by the company's Articles this may be ratified by an ordinary resolution of the members of the type proposed here. If the directors act beyond the powers of the company as set out in the objects clause in its Memorandum of Association, legal advice should be sought. Such a resolution can be proposed should a defect be discovered in the appointment of a director, e.g lack of any shareholding qualification imposed by the Articles of Association or where a director has missed retiring by rotation.

All directors must sign a written resolution.

Proposal of Bonus Issue — Form C20

Company Number: ______________

THE COMPANIES ACT
PRIVATE COMPANY LIMITED BY SHARES
WRITTEN RESOLUTION OF THE BOARD OF DIRECTORS

______________________ LIMITED

Pursuant to the Articles of Association of the company, the undersigned, being all the directors of the company, hereby resolve:

THAT a General Meeting be convened to approve the capitalisation of £______________ of the company's profits by way of the issue of ______________________ share(s) for every ______________________________________ share(s) already held.

Directors' signatures:	Date of each signature:
______________________________	______________________________
______________________________	______________________________
______________________________	______________________________

All directors must sign a written resolution.

Allotment of Shares — Form C21

Company Number: ______________

THE COMPANIES ACT
PRIVATE COMPANY LIMITED BY SHARES
WRITTEN RESOLUTION OF THE BOARD OF DIRECTORS

_______________________ LIMITED

Pursuant to the Articles of Association of the company, the undersigned, being all the directors of the company, hereby resolve THAT the application from ____ annexed hereto for the allotment to him/her of ________ shares of each for an aggregate consideration of £ ___________ / in consideration of ___________________________be accepted and ___________ shares of £ ________________each in the capital of the Company be allotted to ___________________________________ on the terms of his/her application.[1]

Directors' signatures: Date of each signature:

Directors' signatures	Date of each signature
______________________	______________________
______________________	______________________
______________________	______________________

[1] *Check the Articles on whether directors have a separate authority to allot shares – directors can only allot shares if they have the authority to do so. If they do not have the authority, the members can give it to them by passing an ordinary resolution (see Forms E06 and E07). A check should be made to ensure whether or not the statutory pre-emption provisions apply to share allotments; if they do and shares are being allotted to a new shareholder, the existing shareholders should consent to this. Update the register of members. File Companies House form SH01. Prepare and issue a share certificate.*

All directors must sign a written resolution.

Proposal of Dividend — Form C22

Company Number: ______________

THE COMPANIES ACT
PRIVATE COMPANY LIMITED BY SHARES
WRITTEN RESOLUTION OF THE BOARD OF DIRECTORS

______________________ LIMITED

Pursuant to the Articles of Association of the company, the undersigned, being all the directors of the company, hereby resolve:

THAT a General Meeting be convened to declare a dividend of ______ p per share in respect of the year ended ______________________________ on the ordinary shares of ________ each in the capital of the Company payable on ______________________________ to the holders of ordinary shares registered at the close of business on ______________________________ .

Directors' signatures:	Date of each signature:
______________________	______________________
______________________	______________________
______________________	______________________

All directors must sign a written resolution.

Proposal of Purchase of own Shares — Form C23

Company Number: ________________

THE COMPANIES ACT
PRIVATE COMPANY LIMITED BY SHARES
WRITTEN RESOLUTION OF THE BOARD OF DIRECTORS

____________________________ LIMITED

Pursuant to the Articles of Association of the company, the undersigned, being all the directors of the company, hereby resolve:[1]

THAT a General Meeting be convened to propose that the Company purchase _________ of its own shares from ____ on the terms of the contract attached to this resolution, the payment for such shares to be made from the Company's distributable profits / the proceeds of a fresh issue of shares.[2]

Directors' signatures:	Date of each signature:
____________________________________	______________________________________
____________________________________	______________________________________
____________________________________	______________________________________

[1] *A company is allowed to purchase its own shares only in limited circumstances and the directors should not pass this resolution without first seeking the advice of the company's auditors.*

[2] *Delete as appropriate.*

All directors must sign a written resolution.

Proposal of Purchase of own Shares from Capital Form C24

Company Number: ______________

THE COMPANIES ACT
PRIVATE COMPANY LIMITED BY SHARES
WRITTEN RESOLUTION OF THE BOARD OF DIRECTORS

_________________________ LIMITED

Pursuant to the Articles of Association of the company, the undersigned, being all the directors of the company, hereby resolve:

THAT a General Meeting be convened to propose that the Company purchase its own shares, on terms produced to this meeting, and that payment for the purchase shall be made from the capital[1] of the Company.[2]

Directors' signatures:	Date of each signature:
______________________	______________________
______________________	______________________
______________________	______________________

[1] *A company may only purchase its own shares out of capital (i.e. otherwise than from distributable profits or the proceeds of a fresh issue of shares) as a last resort. The rules governing such a purchase and the tax treatment of money paid to shareholders are complex and this resolution should not be used without first seeking the advice of the company's auditors and solicitors.*

[2] *The directors must make a statutory declaration of solvency supported by a report given by the company's auditors within a week of the resolution passed at the General Meeting. A notice to creditors must appear in* The Gazette *(www.gazette.co.uk) and a national newspaper within a week of the members' resolution.*

All directors must sign a written resolution.

Approval and Registration of Transfer of Shares — Form C25

Company Number: _______________

THE COMPANIES ACT
PRIVATE COMPANY LIMITED BY SHARES
WRITTEN RESOLUTION OF THE BOARD OF DIRECTORS

_________________________ LIMITED

Pursuant to the Articles of Association of the company, the undersigned, being all the directors of the company, hereby resolve:

THAT in accordance with the Company's Articles of Association and subject to its being represented duly stamped the directors approve the transfer of __________ shares of __________ each from ____
to ____________________________________ on ______________________________,
THAT the name of ____________________________ be entered in the register of members in respect of the shares transferred to him/her and THAT the Secretary be instructed to prepare a share certificate in respect of the shares transferred and to deliver it to ____.[1]

Directors' signatures:	Date of each signature:
______________________	______________________
______________________	______________________
______________________	______________________

[1] *Check the Articles - they may have a restriction on the transfer of shares. The Model Articles place no restrictions on transfers of fully-paid shares. They may also allow the directors to refuse to register a transfer, although again the Model Articles do not allow them to refuse to register the transfer of fully-paid shares.*

All directors must sign a written resolution.

Proposal that Directors be given Authority to Make a Specific Allotment of Shares for a Specified Purpose Form C26

Company Number: ______________

THE COMPANIES ACT
PRIVATE COMPANY LIMITED BY SHARES
WRITTEN RESOLUTION OF THE BOARD OF DIRECTORS

______________________ LIMITED

Pursuant to the Articles of Association of the company, the undersigned, being all the directors of the company, hereby resolve:

THAT a General Meeting be convened to propose that the directors be given authority to make a specific allotment of up to _____ shares in the capital of the company for the purposes of ____

____.

Directors' signatures:	Date of each signature:
______________________________	______________________________
______________________________	______________________________
______________________________	______________________________

All directors must sign a written resolution.

Proposal that Directors be given Authority to Allot Shares Generally

Form C27

Company Number: ________________

THE COMPANIES ACT
PRIVATE COMPANY LIMITED BY SHARES
WRITTEN RESOLUTION OF THE BOARD OF DIRECTORS

_____________________________ LIMITED

Pursuant to the Articles of Association of the company, the undersigned, being all the directors of the company, hereby resolve:

THAT a General Meeting be convened to propose that the directors be given general and unconditional authority to allot up to ______shares of __________ each in the capital of the company during the period of ____________months/years from the granting of such authority.

Directors' signatures:	Date of each signature:
______________________________	______________________________
______________________________	______________________________
______________________________	______________________________

All directors must sign a written resolution.

Proposal of Revocation of Directors' Authority to Allot Shares

Form C28

Company Number: ______________

THE COMPANIES ACT
PRIVATE COMPANY LIMITED BY SHARES
WRITTEN RESOLUTION OF THE BOARD OF DIRECTORS

_______________________ LIMITED

Pursuant to the Articles of Association of the company, the undersigned, being all the directors of the company, hereby resolve:

THAT a General Meeting be convened to propose that the members revoke the directors' authority to allot shares given in a resolution dated ____________________________.

Directors' signatures:	Date of each signature:
______________________________	______________________________
______________________________	______________________________
______________________________	______________________________

All directors must sign a written resolution.

Proposal to Remove Statutory Pre-Emption Rights — Form C29

Company Number: ______________

THE COMPANIES ACT
PRIVATE COMPANY LIMITED BY SHARES
WRITTEN RESOLUTION OF THE BOARD OF DIRECTORS

______________________ LIMITED

Pursuant to the Articles of Association of the company, the undersigned, being all the directors of the company, hereby resolve:

THAT a General Meeting be convened to propose that the members authorise the directors to allot shares by a resolution passed on ______________________________ as if the Companies Act 2006 did not apply to the allotment.

Directors' signatures:	Date of each signature:
______________________	______________________
______________________	______________________
______________________	______________________

All directors must sign a written resolution.

Proposal of Alteration of Articles — Form C30

Company Number:_______________

THE COMPANIES ACT
PRIVATE COMPANY LIMITED BY SHARES
WRITTEN RESOLUTION OF THE BOARD OF DIRECTORS

___________________________ LIMITED

Pursuant to the Articles of Association of the company the undersigned, being all the directors of the company, hereby resolve:

THAT a General Meeting be convened to authorise the alteration of the Articles as set out below

1) By deletion of Articles ______________________________
and ______________________________
and altering the subsequent numbering accordingly.

2) By the addition of the new Articles as set out in the attached document to be numbered ______________________________
and ______________________________.

Directors' signatures: | Date of each signature:

______________________ | ______________________

______________________ | ______________________

______________________ | ______________________

All directors must sign a written resolution. This resolution may be used to replace the old Table A Articles with the new Companies Act 2006 Model Articles.

Proposal of Alteration of Objects — Form C31

Company Number: ______________

THE COMPANIES ACT
PRIVATE COMPANY LIMITED BY SHARES
WRITTEN RESOLUTION OF THE BOARD OF DIRECTORS

______________________ LIMITED

Pursuant to the Articles of Association of the company the undersigned, being all the directors of the company, hereby resolve:

THAT a General Meeting be convened to authorise the alteration of the objects of the Company contained in the Company's Memorandum of Association in accordance with the document annexed hereto.

Directors' signatures:	Date of each signature:
______________________	______________________
______________________	______________________
______________________	______________________

All directors must sign a written resolution.

Proposal of Alteration of Articles - No Retirement by Rotation

Form C32

Company Number: ______________

THE COMPANIES ACT
PRIVATE COMPANY LIMITED BY SHARES
WRITTEN RESOLUTION OF THE BOARD OF DIRECTORS

______________________ LIMITED

Pursuant to the Articles of Association of the company the undersigned, being all the directors of the company, hereby resolve:

THAT a General Meeting be convened to authorise the alteration of the Articles by the insertion of the wording set out below as new Article no.___ and the renumbering of the subsequent Articles accordingly/in substitution for the existing Article no.___.[1]

The Directors shall not be required to retire by rotation

Directors' signatures:	Date of each signature:
______________________	______________________
______________________	______________________
______________________	______________________

[1] *Delete as appropriate. NB this form is for use only where the Table A regulations referred to in the resolution are presently incorporated in the company's Articles.*

All directors must sign a written resolution.

Proposal of Alteration of Articles - Removal of Chairman's Casting Vote

Form C33

Company Number: ______________

THE COMPANIES ACT
PRIVATE COMPANY LIMITED BY SHARES
WRITTEN RESOLUTION OF THE BOARD OF DIRECTORS

______________________ LIMITED

Pursuant to the Articles of Association of the company the undersigned, being all the directors of the company, hereby resolve:

THAT a General Meeting be convened to authorise the alteration of the Articles by the insertion of the wording set out below as new Article no.___ and the renumbering of the subsequent Articles accordingly/in substitution for the existing Article no.___.[1]

The Chairman shall not have a casting vote.

Directors' signatures:	Date of each signature:
______________________	______________________
______________________	______________________
______________________	______________________

[1] *Delete as appropriate. NB this form is for use only where the Table A regulations referred to in the resolution are presently incorporated in the company's Articles.*

It's a good idea for the chairman to have a casting vote. If he does he should always use it to preserve the status quo.

All directors must sign a written resolution.

Proposal of Alteration of Articles - Director Voting where he has Personal Interest

Form C34

Company Number: ______________

THE COMPANIES ACT
PRIVATE COMPANY LIMITED BY SHARES
WRITTEN RESOLUTION OF THE BOARD OF DIRECTORS

______________________ LIMITED

Pursuant to the Articles of Association of the company the undersigned, being all the directors of the company, hereby resolve:

THAT a General Meeting be convened to authorise the alteration of the Articles by the insertion of the wording set out below as new Article no.___ and the renumbering of the subsequent Articles accordingly/in substitution for the existing Article no.___.[1]

> A Director may vote at any meeting of the Directors or of any Committee of the Directors on any resolution notwithstanding that it in any way concerns or relates to a matter in which he has, directly or indirectly, any kind of interest whatsoever and if he shall vote on any such resolution as aforesaid his vote shall be counted and in relation to any such resolution as aforesaid he shall (whether or not he shall vote on the same) be taken into account in calculating the quorum present at the meeting.

Directors' signatures:	Date of each signature:
______________________	______________________
______________________	______________________
______________________	______________________

[1] *Delete as appropriate. NB this form is for use only where the Table A regulations referred to in the resolution are presently incorporated in the company's Articles.*

All directors must sign a written resolution.

Proposal of Alteration of Articles - Refusal to Register the Transfer of Shares

Form C35

Company Number: ________________

THE COMPANIES ACT
PRIVATE COMPANY LIMITED BY SHARES
WRITTEN RESOLUTION OF THE BOARD OF DIRECTORS

____________________________ LIMITED

Pursuant to the Articles of Association of the company the undersigned, being all the directors of the company, hereby resolve:

THAT a General Meeting be convened to authorise the alteration of the Articles by the insertion of the wording set out below as new Article no.___ and the renumbering of the subsequent Articles accordingly/in substitution for the existing Article no.___.[1]

> The Directors may, in their absolute discretion and without assigning any reason, decline to register the transfer of a share, whether or not it is a fully paid share.

Directors' signatures:	Date of each signature:
____________________________________	____________________________________
____________________________________	____________________________________
____________________________________	____________________________________

[1] *Delete as appropriate. NB this form is for use only where the Table A regulations referred to in the resolution are presently incorporated in the company's Articles.*

All directors must sign a written resolution.

Proposal of Alteration of Articles - Quorum for General Meetings

Form C36

Company Number:_______________

THE COMPANIES ACT
PRIVATE COMPANY LIMITED BY SHARES
WRITTEN RESOLUTION OF THE BOARD OF DIRECTORS

___________________________ LIMITED

Pursuant to the Articles of Association of the company the undersigned, being all the directors of the company, hereby resolve:

THAT a General Meeting be convened to authorise the alteration of the Articles by the insertion of the wording set out below as new Article no.___ and the renumbering of the subsequent Articles accordingly/in substitution for the existing Article no.___.[1]

> If a quorum is not present within half an hour from the time appointed for a General Meeting the General Meeting shall stand adjourned to the same day in the next week at the same time and place or to such other day and at such other time and place as the directors may determine and if at the adjourned General Meeting a quorum is not present within half an hour from the time appointed such adjourned General Meeting shall be dissolved.

Directors' signatures:	Date of each signature:
____________________________________	____________________________________
____________________________________	____________________________________
____________________________________	____________________________________

[1] *Delete as appropriate. NB this form is for use only where the Table A regulations referred to in the resolution are presently incorporated in the company's Articles.*

A quorum for a private company is normally considered to be two unless it is a single member company.

All directors must sign a written resolution.

Proposal of Alteration of Articles - Number of Directors Form C37

Company Number:_______________

THE COMPANIES ACT
PRIVATE COMPANY LIMITED BY SHARES
WRITTEN RESOLUTION OF THE BOARD OF DIRECTORS

____________________________ LIMITED

Pursuant to the Articles of Association of the company the undersigned, being all the directors of the company, hereby resolve:

THAT a General Meeting be convened to authorise the alteration of the Articles by the insertion of the wording set out below as new Article no.___ and the renumbering of the subsequent Articles accordingly/in substitution for the existing Article no.___.[1]

> The maximum number and minimum number respectively of the directors may be determined from time to time by ordinary resolution in General Meeting of the company. Subject to and in default of any such determination there shall be no maximum number of directors and the minimum number of directors shall be one. Whensoever the minimum number of directors shall be one, a sole director shall have authority to exercise all the powers and discretions expressed by these Articles to be vested in the directors generally and regulation 89 in Table A shall be modified accordingly.

Directors' signatures:	Date of each signature:
______________________	______________________
______________________	______________________
______________________	______________________

[1] *Delete as appropriate. NB this form is for use only where the Table A regulations referred to in the resolution are presently incorporated in the company's Articles.*

All directors must sign a written resolution.

Proposal of Alteration of Articles - Alternate Directors Form C38

Company Number: ______________

THE COMPANIES ACT
PRIVATE COMPANY LIMITED BY SHARES
WRITTEN RESOLUTION OF THE BOARD OF DIRECTORS

________________________ LIMITED

Pursuant to the Articles of Association of the company the undersigned, being all the directors of the company, hereby resolve:

THAT a General Meeting be convened to authorise the alteration of the Articles by the insertion of the wording set out below as new Article no.___ and the renumbering of the subsequent Articles accordingly/in substitution for the existing Article no.___.[1]

> An alternate director shall not be entitled to receive any remuneration from the company, save that he may be paid by the company such part (if any) of the remuneration otherwise payable to his appointor as such appointor may by notice in writing to the company from time to time direct.

Directors' signatures: Date of each signature:

______________________________ ______________________________

______________________________ ______________________________

______________________________ ______________________________

[1] *Delete as appropriate. NB this form is for use only where the Table A regulations referred to in the resolution are presently incorporated in the company's Articles.*

All directors must sign a written resolution.

Proposal of Alteration of Articles - Weighted Voting Rights Form C39

Company Number:_______________

THE COMPANIES ACT
PRIVATE COMPANY LIMITED BY SHARES
WRITTEN RESOLUTION OF THE BOARD OF DIRECTORS

__________________________ LIMITED

Pursuant to the Articles of Association of the company the undersigned, being all the directors of the company, hereby resolve:

THAT a General Meeting be convened to authorise the alteration of the Articles by the insertion of the wording set out below as new Article no.___ and the renumbering of the subsequent Articles accordingly/in substitution for the existing Article no.___.[1]

Every director for the time being of the company shall have the following rights:

a) if at any General Meeting a resolution is proposed to remove him from office, he shall be entitled to demand a poll and on that poll he shall have when voting against such resolution ____[2] votes for each share of which he is the holder; and

b) if at any General Meeting a poll is duly demanded on a resolution to delete or amend the provisions of this Article, he shall be entitled to demand a poll and on that poll he shall have when voting against such resolution ____[3] votes for each share of which he is the holder.

Directors' signatures:	Date of each signature:
______________________	______________________
______________________	______________________
______________________	______________________

[1] *Delete as appropriate. This Article will have the effect of preventing the directors (as long as they are also shareholders) from being removed from office.*

[2] *Insert the relevant number which will ensure that each director has more than 50% of the votes in this situation.*

[3] *Insert the relevant number which will ensure that each director has more than 75% of the votes in this situation.*

NB this form is for use only where the Table A regulations referred to in the resolution are presently incorporated in the company's Articles.

All directors must sign a written resolution.

Proposal of Alteration of Articles - Authority to Allot Shares Form C40

Company Number:_______________

THE COMPANIES ACT
PRIVATE COMPANY LIMITED BY SHARES
WRITTEN RESOLUTION OF THE BOARD OF DIRECTORS

___________________________ LIMITED

Pursuant to the Articles of Association of the company the undersigned, being all the directors of the company, hereby resolve:

THAT a General Meeting be convened to authorise the alteration of the Articles by the insertion of the wording set out below as new Article no.___ and the renumbering of the subsequent Articles accordingly/in substitution for the existing Article no.___.[1]

> The directors are generally and unconditionally authorised for the purposes of s.80 of the Companies Act to exercise any powers of the company to allot and grant rights to subscribe for or convert securities into shares of the company up to the amount of the authorised share capital with which the company is incorporated at any time or times during the period of the five years from the date of incorporation and the directors may after that period allot any shares or grant any such rights under this authority in pursuance of an offer or agreement so to do made by the company within that period. The authority hereby given may at any time be renewed, revoked or varied by ordinary resolution of the company in General Meeting.

Directors' signatures:	Date of each signature:
______________________________	______________________________
______________________________	______________________________
______________________________	______________________________

[1] *Delete as appropriate. NB this form is for use only where the Table A regulations referred to in the resolution are presently incorporated in the company's Articles.*

All directors must sign a written resolution.

Proposal of Adoption of New Articles Form C41

Company Number: ______________

THE COMPANIES ACT
PRIVATE COMPANY LIMITED BY SHARES
WRITTEN RESOLUTION OF THE BOARD OF DIRECTORS

______________________ LIMITED

Pursuant to the Articles of Association of the company the undersigned, being all the directors of the company, hereby resolve:

THAT a General Meeting be convened to authorise the adoption of new Articles of Association in the form annexed hereto.

Directors' signatures:	Date of each signature:
______________________	______________________
______________________	______________________
______________________	______________________

All directors must sign a written resolution.

Proposal of Name Change — Form C42

Company Number: ______________

THE COMPANIES ACT
PRIVATE COMPANY LIMITED BY SHARES
WRITTEN RESOLUTION OF THE BOARD OF DIRECTORS

______________________ LIMITED

Pursuant to the Articles of Association of the company the undersigned, being all the directors of the company, hereby resolve:

THAT a General Meeting be convened to propose that the name of the company be changed to ____
with effect from ____.[1]

Directors' signatures: | Date of each signature:
___________________ | ___________________
___________________ | ___________________
___________________ | ___________________

[1] Copy of special resolution passed at General Meeting and amended print of the company's Memorandum and Articles of Association will need to be filed at Companies House within 15 days of being passed together with the statutory change of name fee. If it is intended to have a change of name effective from a particular day, Companies House should be contacted before putting the resolution to the members.

All directors must sign a written resolution.

Adoption of Trading Name Form C43

Company Number:_______________

THE COMPANIES ACT
PRIVATE COMPANY LIMITED BY SHARES
WRITTEN RESOLUTION OF THE BOARD OF DIRECTORS

_______________________ LIMITED

Pursuant to the Articles of Association of the company the undersigned, being all the directors of the company, hereby resolve:

THAT the Company should trade under the name '______________________________' and that the Secretary be instructed to ensure compliance with the statutory disclosure requirements in the Business Names Act 1985.

Directors' signatures:	Date of each signature:
______________________	______________________
______________________	______________________
______________________	______________________

All directors must sign a written resolution.

Proposal that Company Re-Register as PLC — Form C44

Company Number: ______________

THE COMPANIES ACT
PRIVATE COMPANY LIMITED BY SHARES
WRITTEN RESOLUTION OF THE BOARD OF DIRECTORS

________________________ LIMITED

Pursuant to the Articles of Association of the company, the undersigned, being all the directors of the company, hereby resolve:

THAT a General Meeting be convened to propose that the company be re-registered as a public company as defined in of the Companies Act 2006.[1]

Directors' signatures:	Date of each signature:
______________________	______________________
______________________	______________________
______________________	______________________

[1] *To re-register as a PLC a company must have a minimum of two shareholders and two directors and an authorised share capital of at least £50,000 and each share must be paid up at least as to 25% of its nominal value and the whole of any premium. The company must send to Companies House an application to re-register, a signed copy of the special resolution passed by the members, new Memorandum and Articles, a copy of the latest balance sheet, an unqualified auditors report on the latest balance sheet, a further report from the auditors stating that the company's net assets are not less than its capital as shown in the balance sheet and a statutory declaration from a director stating that the net asset position is maintained and the statutory requirements have been complied with.*

All directors must sign a written resolution.

Change of Address of Registered Office — Form C45

Company Number: ________________

THE COMPANIES ACT
PRIVATE COMPANY LIMITED BY SHARES
WRITTEN RESOLUTION OF THE BOARD OF DIRECTORS

______________________ LIMITED

Pursuant to the Articles of Association of the company the undersigned, being all the directors of the company, hereby resolve:

THAT the registered office of the Company be changed to ______________________

____

and the Secretary be instructed to file the necessary return with the Registrar of Companies.[1]

Directors' signatures:	Date of each signature:
______________________	______________________
______________________	______________________
______________________	______________________

[1] *File Companies House form AD01. The registered address of the company cannot be changed outside the country stated in its Memorandum of Association.*

All directors must sign a written resolution.

Adoption of Company Seal — Form C46

Company Number: ______________

THE COMPANIES ACT
PRIVATE COMPANY LIMITED BY SHARES
WRITTEN RESOLUTION OF THE BOARD OF DIRECTORS

____________________ LIMITED

Pursuant to the Articles of Association of the company the undersigned, being all the directors of the company, hereby resolve:

THAT the seal, an impression of which is affixed to this resolution, be adopted as the common seal of the Company.[1]

Directors' signatures:	Date of each signature:
____________________	____________________
____________________	____________________
____________________	____________________

[1] A company is not required to have a seal.

All directors must sign a written resolution.

Change of Accounting Reference Date — Form C47

Company Number: ______________

THE COMPANIES ACT
PRIVATE COMPANY LIMITED BY SHARES
WRITTEN RESOLUTION OF THE BOARD OF DIRECTORS

______________________ **LIMITED**

Pursuant to the Articles of Association of the company the undersigned, being all the directors of the company, hereby resolve:

THAT the accounting reference date of the Company be changed from ______________________ to ______________________ and the Secretary be instructed to file the necessary return with Companies House.[1]

Directors' signatures:	Date of each signature:
______________________	______________________
______________________	______________________
______________________	______________________

[1] *File Companies House form AA01. The maximum allowable accounting reference period is 18 months. The period cannot be extended more than once every five years except in certain specified circumstances. There are no restrictions on how often an accounting reference period can be shortened.*

All directors must sign a written resolution.

Proposal of Voluntary Liquidation where Company is Insolvent

Form C48

Company Number: ______________

THE COMPANIES ACT
PRIVATE COMPANY LIMITED BY SHARES
WRITTEN RESOLUTION OF THE BOARD OF DIRECTORS

______________________ LIMITED

Pursuant to the Articles of Association of the company the undersigned, being all the directors of the company, hereby resolve:

THAT the company being unable to continue its business by reason of its liabilities a General Meeting be convened for the purpose of passing a special resolution to effect a creditors voluntary winding up of the company.[1]

Directors' signatures:	Date of each signature:
______________________	______________________
______________________	______________________
______________________	______________________

[1] The directors must take expert advice from a licensed insolvency practitioner as soon as it appears that the company may be unable to continue its business by reason of its liabilities. There are serious criminal sanctions if a director fails to take every step to minimise the potential loss to the company's creditors once he knows or ought to have known that there is no reasonable prospect of the company avoiding an insolvent liquidation.

All directors must sign a written resolution.

Proposal of Voluntary Liquidation where Company is Solvent

Form C49

Company Number: ________________

THE COMPANIES ACT
PRIVATE COMPANY LIMITED BY SHARES
WRITTEN RESOLUTION OF THE BOARD OF DIRECTORS

________________________ LIMITED

Pursuant to the Articles of Association of the company the undersigned, being all the directors of the company, hereby resolve:

THAT a General Meeting be convened for the purpose of passing an special resolution to effect a members' voluntary winding up of the company.[1]

Directors' signatures: Date of each signature:

____________________ ____________________

____________________ ____________________

____________________ ____________________

[1] *The directors must make a statutory declaration as to the company's solvency within the period of 5 weeks prior to the General Meeting (see footnote to Form E17).The directors should take the advice of the company's auditors and a licensed insolvency practitioner before making the statutory declaration and passing this resolution. If they are unable to make such a declaration the winding up will be a creditors' voluntary winding up.*

All directors must sign a written resolution.

Application for Administration Order — Form C50

Company Number: ______________

THE COMPANIES ACT
PRIVATE COMPANY LIMITED BY SHARES
WRITTEN RESOLUTION OF THE BOARD OF DIRECTORS

______________________ LIMITED

Pursuant to the Articles of Association of the company the undersigned, being all the directors of the company, hereby resolve:[1]

THAT the company being/being likely to become unable to pay its debts an application be made to the court for an administration order, in order to achieve[2] __________________

____

____

Directors' signatures:	Date of each signature:
______________________	______________________
______________________	______________________
______________________	______________________

[1] *The directors should take the advice of a licensed insolvency practitioner before passing this resolution. A petition to the court for an administration order must be supported by an affidavit and an independent report on the company's affairs. The order will only be granted if the court is satisfied that the company is or is likely to become unable to pay its debts and an order is likely to achieve one or more of the following: (a) the survival of the company, and the whole or any part of its undertaking as a going concern, (b) the approval of a voluntary arrangement with creditors, (c) the sanctioning of a scheme of arrangement, and (d) a more advantageous realisation of the company's assets than would be effected on a winding up. Any creditor who has validly appointed an administrative receiver prior to the court's consideration of the petition must consent before an order can be made.*

[2] *Specify one or more of the outcomes listed in (a) to (d) in footnote 1 above.*

All directors must sign a written resolution.

Approval of Auditors' Remuneration for Audit — Form C51

Company Number: ________________

THE COMPANIES ACT
PRIVATE COMPANY LIMITED BY SHARES
WRITTEN RESOLUTION OF THE BOARD OF DIRECTORS

____________________________ LIMITED

Pursuant to the Articles of Association of the company the undersigned, being all the directors of the company, hereby resolve:

THAT the remuneration of the auditors for the audit for the accounting period ended

____

be agreed at £ ________________ inclusive of expenses.[1]

Directors' signatures:	Date of each signature:
____________________________	____________________________
____________________________	____________________________
____________________________	____________________________

[1] *The directors may only pass this resolution if they have been given the authority to do so by the members in General Meeting. All directors must sign a written resolution.*

Approval of Auditors' Remuneration for Services and Advice

Form C52

Company Number: ______________

THE COMPANIES ACT
PRIVATE COMPANY LIMITED BY SHARES
WRITTEN RESOLUTION OF THE BOARD OF DIRECTORS

______________________ LIMITED

Pursuant to the Articles of Association of the company the undersigned, being all the directors of the company, hereby resolve:

THAT the remuneration of the auditors for services and advice for the accounting period ended ____

be agreed at £ ______________ inclusive of expenses.

Directors' signatures:	Date of each signature:
______________________________	______________________________
______________________________	______________________________
______________________________	______________________________

All directors must sign a written resolution.

Registration for VAT — Form C53

Company Number: ______________

THE COMPANIES ACT
PRIVATE COMPANY LIMITED BY SHARES
WRITTEN RESOLUTION OF THE BOARD OF DIRECTORS

____________________ LIMITED

Pursuant to the Articles of Association of the company the undersigned, being all the directors of the company, hereby resolve:

To instruct the Secretary to register the Company with H.M. Revenue & Customs for VAT purposes.[1]

Directors' signatures:	Date of each signature:
______________________________	______________________________
______________________________	______________________________
______________________________	______________________________

[1] *Registration is obligatory if the company's taxable turnover in the past 12 months or less exceeds £82,000 (2015/16 threshold), or if there are reasonable grounds for believing that its taxable turnover will exceed this amount in the next 30 days. The directors should take expert tax advice on this matter.*

All directors must sign a written resolution.

Issue of Debenture Form C54

Company Number: ______________

THE COMPANIES ACT
PRIVATE COMPANY LIMITED BY SHARES
WRITTEN RESOLUTION OF THE BOARD OF DIRECTORS

______________________ LIMITED

Pursuant to the Articles of Association of the company the undersigned, being all the directors of the company, hereby resolve:

To issue a debenture dated ____________________________________ in favour of ____

on the terms produced to this meeting and that any director be authorised to execute such debenture on behalf of the company.[1]

Directors' signatures: Date of each signature:

______________________________ ______________________________

______________________________ ______________________________

______________________________ ______________________________

[1] *It is the company's responsibility to register with Companies House any charge over the company's assets contained in the debenture within 21 days of the creation of the charge on Companies House form MG01. Details of the charge must also be entered in the company's register of charges. A fee is payable to Companies House on the registration of a charge. While the company is primarily responsible for the registration of the charge, anyone who is interested in the charge can register details at Companies House.*

All directors must sign a written resolution.

Proposal of Approval of Substantial Property Transaction Form C55

Company Number: _______________

THE COMPANIES ACT
PRIVATE COMPANY LIMITED BY SHARES
WRITTEN RESOLUTION OF THE BOARD OF DIRECTORS

___________________________ LIMITED

Pursuant to the Articles of Association of the company the undersigned, being all the directors of the company, hereby resolve:

THAT in accordance with the Companies Act 2006 a General Meeting be convened to propose that the members approve a substantial property transaction involving ______, being a director of the company, the terms of which are attached.[1]

Directors' signatures:	Date of each signature:
___________________________	___________________________
___________________________	___________________________
___________________________	___________________________

[1] The Companies Act 2006 requires any arrangement between a company and a director involving the transfer, either from the company to the director or from the director to the company, of a non-cash asset the value of which exceeds £100,000 or 10% of the company's net assets (provided it is not less than £2,000) to be approved by the company's members.

All directors must sign a written resolution.

SECTION D

General Meetings

The forms in this section are designed to be used in connection with a meeting of the company's shareholders. You should pay careful attention to the requirements relating to the notice periods for these meetings (see Introduction, page 4). You should also check the company's Articles to make sure that the requirements for a quorum to be present and the correct voting procedures are observed.

The text of the actual resolutions you require may be selected from those set out in Section E and then inserted into the notices and minutes as appropriate. Where a document is referred to as being attached to the written resolution this should be replaced in the resolution in minute form by a reference to the relevant document being 'produced to the meeting'.

Annual General Meeting

Under recent legislation you do not need to hold an AGM anymore, but most companies will probably continue to do so.

D01 Notice of Annual General Meeting—Announces the time, place and agenda of the annual general meeting. It must be given to all members entitled to attend 14 days prior to the meeting. The basic agenda includes adopting accounts and reports of the directors and auditors, declaring a dividend, (re-)appointing auditors, electing directors, and confirming appointments to the board.

D02 Consent to short notice for an AGM—Members must give approval for an annual general meeting called on short notice.

D03 Appointment of a proxy for an AGM—A member allowed to vote at an annual meeting may appoint a non-member to vote in his place.

D04 Minutes of Annual General Meeting—An official recording of the proceedings at an annual general meeting.

General Meetings

D05 Notice of General Meeting—Announces the time, place and agenda of a general meeting that is not the annual general meeting. It must be given to all members entitled to attend 14 days prior to the meeting.

D06 **Consent to short notice for a general meeting**—Members must give approval for a general meeting called on short notice.

D07 **Appointment of proxy for a general meeting**—A member allowed to vote at a general meeting may appoint a non-member to vote in his place.

D08 **Minutes of a General Meeting**—An official recording of the proceedings at a general meeting.

Other Notices

D09 **Special notice of resolution to remove a director**—Notice to be given no later than 14 days prior to the date of the meeting to remove a director.

D10 **Notice of meeting to remove a director**—Notifies members of a general meeting to propose removal of a director.

D11 **Notice of resolution given by the company to the director**—Notifies the director being removed.

D12 **Special notice of resolution to remove auditors**—Notice to be given to the company no later than 14 days prior to the date of the meeting to remove auditors before their term of office has expired.

D13 **Notice of meeting to remove auditors**—Notifies members of a general meeting to propose removal of auditors before their term of office has expired.

Notice of Annual General Meeting Form D01

______________________ LIMITED

NOTICE IS HEREBY GIVEN that the ANNUAL GENERAL MEETING of the above-named company will be held at ______________________________________ on ______________________________________ at _________ am/pm for the following purposes.

1. The company's accounts and reports of the directors and auditors for the period____________to ____________will be received and considered .
2. To declare a dividend.
3. To elect directors in place of those retiring (see the directors report).
4. To confirm appointments to the board.
5. To reappoint ______________________________ as auditors of the company until the next general meeting at which accounts are laid before the company, at a fee to be agreed with the board of directors.

Dated

By order of the board

Secretary

Registered office:____

A member entitled to attend and vote at the meeting convened by this Notice is entitled to appoint a proxy to attend and vote on a poll in his/her place. A proxy need not be a member of the company.

At meetings of a private limited company a proxy has the same right as a member to speak on a matter.

Consent to Short Notice for an AGM — Form D02

______________________ **LIMITED**

We, the undersigned, being 90% of the members of the company having a right to attend and vote at the annual general meeting of the company to be held on ____ at ___________ am/pm., hereby agree:

(a) to accept shorter notice of the said meeting than the period of notice prescribed by s 307 of Companies Act 2006; and

(b) to accept service of the documents specified in the Companies Act 2006 less than fourteen days before the date of the meeting.

Dated

____

____

____

Appointment of a Proxy for an AGM — Form D03

________________________ LIMITED

FORM OF PROXY FOR USE BY ORDINARY SHAREHOLDERS
FOR THE ANNUAL GENERAL MEETING ON

____

I __________________________ of ________________________being a member of the above-named company, hereby appoint ____________________________ of ______________________ or, failing him/her, ________________________ of __________________________ or failing him/her the duly appointed chairman of the meeting as my proxy at the annual general meeting of the company to be held on __________________________ and at any adjournment thereof and to vote on my behalf as directed below.

RESOLUTIONS	For	Against
1. [*Insert text of resolution*]	☐	☐
2. [*Insert text of resolution*]	☐	☐

Dated

____

Signature

____

Notes:

a) This form of proxy, together with the power of attorney or other authority (if any) under which it was signed, or an office or notarially certified copy thereof, must be lodged [at the company's registered office] not later than 48 hours before the meeting.
b) A proxy need not be a member of the company.
c) In the case of joint holders the signature of the first-named will be accepted to the exclusion of all others.
d) In the case of a corporation this form of proxy should be under its common seal or under the hand of an officer or attorney duly authorised.
e) Any alterations to this form of proxy should be initialled.
f) The completion of this form of proxy will not preclude the member from attending and voting in person if he/she so wishes.

Minutes of Annual General Meeting Form D04

_____________________ **LIMITED**

MINUTES of the annual general meeting of the company held at ______________________________ on ____________ at ____________ a.m./p.m.

PRESENT ____ (in the chair)

____

IN ATTENDANCE ____

____

1. The Chairman announced that consents to the meeting being held at short notice had been received from all of the members of the company having a right to attend and vote at the meeting.
2. The Chairman declared that a quorum was present.
3. It was unanimously agreed that the notice convening the meeting should be taken as read.
4. The Chairman submitted the company's profit and loss account for the period ended ____________ , together with the balance sheet as at that date and it was resolved that the accounts as submitted to the meeting be and are received.[1]
5. It was resolved that a final dividend of _____ p per share in respect of the year ended ______________________________ be declared on the ordinary shares of ______________ each in the capital of the company, payable on ______________________________ to the holders of ordinary shares registered at the close of business on ______________________________.
6. It was resolved that ____, the director(s) retiring by rotation, be re-elected a director(s) of the company.
7. It was resolved that the appointment of ______________________________ to the board on ______________________________ be confirmed.
8. It was resolved that ______________________________ be reappointed auditors of the company until the conclusion of the next general meeting at which accounts are laid before the company, at a fee to be agreed with the board of directors.
9. The meeting then ended.

____

Chairman

[1] *There is no requirement for the accounts to be approved by the shareholders; they need only be laid before them in general meeting*

Notice of General Meeting

Form D05

__________________________ LIMITED

NOTICE IS HEREBY GIVEN that a GENERAL MEETING of the above-named company will be held at ____
on ____ at _________ am/pm to consider and, if thought fit, pass the following resolutions which will be proposed as to resolutions ____________________________________ as special resolutions and as to resolutions ______________________________ as ordinary resolutions of the company.

ORDINARY RESOLUTION

[*insert text of resolutions*] ____
____

SPECIAL RESOLUTIONS

[*insert text of resolutions*][1] ____
____

Dated

____

Signature

____

[1] *For the text of various example resolutions see Section E*

50% is the majority required for an ordinary resolution. 75% is the majority required for a special resolution.

A member entitled to attend and vote at the meeting convened by this Notice is entitled to appoint a proxy to attend and vote in his/her place. A proxy need not be a member of the company.

Consent to Short Notice for a general meeting — Form D06

____________________ LIMITED

We, the undersigned, being a majority in number of the members of the company holding not less than 90% of the issued share capital having a right to attend and vote at the general meeting of the company to be held on ____________ at ____________am/pm., HEREBY CONSENT to the convening and holding of such meeting and the proposing and passing thereat of the resolutions set out in the notice of meeting notwithstanding that the meeting has been convened by less than the statutory period of notice.

Dated

____

____

____

Appointment of a Proxy for a general meeting — Form D07

________________________ LIMITED

FORM OF PROXY FOR USE BY ORDINARY SHAREHOLDERS
FOR THE GENERAL MEETING TO BE HELD ON

____

I ____________________________ of ________________________ being a member of the above-named company, hereby appoint ____________________________ of _______________________ or, failing him/her, ___________________________ of ___________________________ or failing him/her the duly appointed chairman of the meeting as my proxy at the general meeting of the company to be held on _____________________________ and at any adjournment thereof and to vote on my behalf as directed below.

RESOLUTIONS

Please indicate how you wish your proxy to vote by placing an 'X' in the appropriate box. Unless otherwise indicated the proxy will exercise his discretion as to how he votes and whether he abstains from voting.

		For	Against
1.	[*Insert text of resolution*]	☐	☐
2.	[*Insert text of resolution*]	☐	☐

Dated

____

Signature

____

Notes:

a) This form of proxy, together with the power of attorney or other authority (if any) under which it was signed, or an office or notarially certified copy thereof, must be lodged [at the company's registered office] not later than 48 hours before the meeting.
b) A proxy need not be a member of the company.
c) In the case of joint holders the signature of the first-named will be accepted to the exclusion of all others.
d) In the case of a corporation this form of proxy should be under its common seal or under the hand of an officer or attorney duly authorised.
e) Any alterations to this form of proxy should be initialled.
f) The completion of this form of proxy will not preclude the member from attending and voting in person if he/she so wishes.

Minutes of General Meeting — Form D08

____________________ **LIMITED**

MINUTES of an general meeting of the company held at____________________ on ____________ at __________ a.m./p.m.

PRESENT ______________________________________ (in the chair)

____

IN ATTENDANCE ______________________________________

____

1. The Chairman confirmed that notice of the meeting had been given to all the members of the company having a right to attend and vote at the meeting OR announced that consents to the meeting being held at short notice had been received from a majority in number of the members holding not less than 90% of the issued share capital having a right to attend and vote at the meeting.
2. The Chairman declared that a quorum was present.
3. It was unanimously agreed that the notice convening the meeting should be taken as read.
4. The Chairman proposed the following resolution as an ordinary/special resolution:

   ____

   ____

   ____

5. The Chairman put the resolution to the meeting, took the vote on a show of hands[1] and declared the resolution passed as an ordinary/special resolution of the company.[2]
6. The meeting then ended.

____

Chairman

[1] *If a poll is validly demanded, the resolution may not be passed or blocked on a show of hands. The circumstances in which a poll may be demanded and the way in which it should be conducted are set out in the Articles (in Table A the relevant provisions are Articles 46-52). The fact that a poll has been demanded, by whom and the result of the poll should be recorded in the minutes.*

[2] *Repeat points 4 and 5 for each resolution.*

Special Notice of Resolution to Remove a Director — Form D09

______________________ **LIMITED**

The Directors

____

In accordance with section 168 of the Companies Act 2006, I hereby give notice of my intention to move the following resolution at a general meeting of the company, to be held not earlier than 28 days from the date of this notice.[1]

ORDINARY RESOLUTION

That ____ be and is hereby removed from office as a director of the company.

Dated

____

____

____

[1] *This notice must be given by a member and left at the company's registered office at least 28 days before the general meeting. On receipt of this notice the company must send a copy to the director concerned - see Form D11. The company must give notice of this resolution to the members when it gives them notice of the meeting (or, if that is not practicable, either by advertisement in a newspaper having an appropriate circulation or in any other mode allowed by the Articles, not less than 21 days before the meeting) - see Form D10.*

Notice of Meeting to Remove a Director — Form D10

_______________________ **LIMITED**

NOTICE IS HEREBY GIVEN that a general meeting of the company will be held at the registered office of the company on ______________________________[1] at __________ am/pm to consider and, if thought fit, pass the following resolution as an ordinary resolution, special notice of this resolution having been given in accordance with the Companies Act 2006.[2]

ORDINARY RESOLUTION

That ____ be and is hereby removed from office as a director of the company.

Dated

____

By order of the board

____

Secretary
Registered office:______________________________________

A member entitled to attend and vote at the meeting convened by this Notice is entitled to appoint a proxy to attend and vote [on a poll] in his/her place. A proxy need not be a member of the company.

[1] *Date of meeting must be at least 28 days after date of receipt of special notice.*

[2] *If the company has received any representations from the director in respect of his removal this notice should state this fact and a copy of the representations should be sent to all the shareholders. File Companies House form TM01 after passing of resolution.*

Notice of Resolution given by Company to the Director[1] Form D11

______________________ LIMITED

To:

Date:

Dear Sir

I am writing to inform you that the enclosed special notice has been received, in accordance with the Companies Act 2006, and that the following ordinary resolution will be proposed at a general meeting of the company on ________________________
at ________ am/pm at the registered office of this company.

ORDINARY RESOLUTION

That ____ be and is hereby removed from office as director of the company.

In accordance with the Companies Act 2006 you are entitled to be heard at the meeting and may request that representations in writing made by you be sent to all members of the company to whom notices of the meetings are sent. If you wish representations to be sent may I receive them not later than ______________________________________.

Yours faithfully

____

[1] *Send as soon as special notice is received. Enclose a copy of the special notice.*

Special Notice of Resolution to Remove Auditors — Form D12

______________________ LIMITED

The Directors

____

In accordance with the Companies Act 2006, I hereby give special notice of my intention to move the following resolution at a general meeting of the company, to be held not earlier than 28 days from the date of this notice.[1]

ORDINARY RESOLUTION

That ____ be and are hereby removed from their office as auditors of the company.

Dated

____

____

____

[1] *This notice must be given by a member and left at the company's registered office at least 28 days before the general meeting. On receipt of this notice the company must send a copy to the auditors see Form C08. The company must give notice of this resolution to the members when it gives them notice of the meeting (or, if that is not practicable, either by advertisement in a newspaper having an appropriate circulation or in any other mode allowed by the Articles, not less than 21 days before the meeting).*

Notice of Meeting to Remove Auditors — Form D13

______________________ LIMITED

NOTICE IS HEREBY GIVEN that a general meeting of the company will be held at the registered office of the company on ______________________________[1] at ____________ am/pm to consider and, if thought fit, pass the following resolution as an ordinary resolution, special notice of this resolution having been given in accordance with the Companies Act 2006.[2]

ORDINARY RESOLUTION

That ____ be and are hereby removed from their office as auditors of the company.

Dated

____

By order of the board

____

Secretary

Registered office:____________________________________

A member entitled to attend and vote at the meeting convened by this Notice is entitled to appoint a proxy to attend and vote [on a poll] in his/her place. A proxy need not be a member of the company.

[1] *Date of meeting must be at least 28 days from date of receipt of special notice.*

[2] *If the company has received any representations from the auditors in respect of their removal this notice should state this fact and a copy of the representations should be sent to all the shareholders. File Companies House form AA03 within 14 days of passing resolution.*

SECTION E

Shareholders' Resolutions

Shareholders' resolutions are classified as 'ordinary' or 'special' depending on their intention. An ordinary resolution (OR), whether written or passed at a meeting, requires a majority approval (i.e. more than 50 per cent). A special resolution (SR), whether written or passed at a meeting, requires a three-quarters majority of the votes cast at a meeting, which requires at least 21 clear days' notice. Shareholders' resolutions may be passed at annual or general meetings or by passing a written resolution, as provided in this section. The company number is written on the certificate of incorporation you received from the Companies House.

Passing the written resolution

If the written resolution procedure is used, the directors must notify the company's auditors, if appointed, of the contents of the resolution or send them a copy of it at or before the time it is supplied to the members for signature, unless the Articles permit a written resolution to be passed and do not require the auditors to be notified in this way. A written resolution must be signed by over 50% of the members, (75% in the case of special resolutions), although they may sign separate copies. It becomes effective on the signature of the last member and should be dated with the date on which that member signed.

After the resolution has been passed

Once the written resolution has been passed it should be placed in the company's minute book. Certain resolutions should filed at Companies House e.g. all special resolutions and some ordinary resolutions, such as the giving of authority to allot shares under the Companies Act 2006. Where this is required a separate print of a resolution passed at a meeting should be prepared and signed by the chairman, while if a written resolution has been passed the filing of a copy of the signed document will generally suffice.

E01 Standard written resolution—This is the basic format for a shareholders' resolution to be passed without holding a general meeting.

Appointments and Removals

E02 Appointment of director (OR)—Resolves to appoint a new director.

E03 Fixing of maximum number of directors (OR)—Resolves to limit the number of directors.

Shares

E04 Reduction of share capital (SR)—Resolves to reduce share capital by dividing shares and reducing the nominal amount of each share.

E05 Allotment of shares - specific authority (OR)—Resolves to give directors authority to make a specific allotment of a certain number for a specified purpose.

E06 Allotment of shares - general authority (OR)—Resolves to give directors general and unconditional authority to allot a certain number of shares for a period of up to five years or, if the relevant resolution is in place, for an indefinite period.

E07 Removal of authority to allot shares (OR)—Resolves to revoke directors' authority to allot ordinary shares

E08 Declaration of dividend (OR)—Resolves to pay shareholders a dividend.

E09 Removal of statutory pre-emption rights - general (SR)—Resolves to remove the statutory right of existing shareholders to be offered any new shares which are to be allotted before they are allotted to anyone else, in respect of any allotment made pursuant to a general section 80 authority conferred on the directors (see Form E07).

E10 Removal of statutory pre-emption rights in respect of specified allotment (SR)—Resolves to remove the right of existing shareholders to be offered any new shares which are to be allotted before they are allotted to anyone else in respect of a specified allotment.

E11 Purchase of own shares (SR)—Resolves to approve the company's purchase of shares otherwise than out of capital.

E12 Purchase of own shares from capital (SR)—Resolves to approve the company's purchase of shares out of capital.

E13 Bonus issue (OR)—Resolves to issue shares by way of bonus issue.

Financial

E14 Approval of substantial property transaction (OR)—Resolves to approve a substantial property transaction involving a director.

E15 Approval of directors' remuneration (OR)—Resolves to pay a director a designated amount.

E16 Voluntary liquidation - solvent (SR)—Resolves to begin the winding up of the company.

E17 Voluntary liquidation - insolvent (SR)—Resolves to begin winding up because the company is insolvent and unable to pay its debts.

E18 Application for administration order (OR)—Resolves to apply for an administrator to be appointed to run the company while it is unable to pay its debts.

Change Constitution

E19 Reregistration as public company (SR)—Resolves to reregister company as a public company.

E20 Change of company name (SR)—Resolves to change the company name.

E21 Change of Articles (SR)—Resolves to alter certain Articles of Association.

E22 Adoption of new Articles of Association (SR)—Resolves to replace entire Articles of Association.

E23 Change of objects (SR)—Resolves to alter certain objects of the company as set out in the Memorandum of Association.

Directors

E24 Approval of compensation payment (OR)—Resolves to approve payment to a retiring director.

E25 Approval of service contract exceeding two years' duration (OR)—Resolves to approve a director's service contract of more than two years.

E26 Ratification of acts of directors beyond the powers delegated to them under the Articles (OR)—Resolves to ratify acts of directors which were beyond the powers delegated to them.

E27 Allowing of director to vote on contracts where has personal interest (OR)—Resolves to approve a director voting on a matter in which he has a personal interest.

Altering the Articles

E28 Alteration of Articles - no retirement by rotation (SR)—changes Articles so that directors are not required to retire by rotation.

E29 Alteration of Articles - removal of chairman's casting vote (SR)—changes Articles so that the chairman does not have a casting vote at board meetings.

E30 Alteration of Articles - director voting where personal interest (SR)—changes Articles so that a director can vote at a any meeting or on any resolution where he has a personal interest.

E31 Alteration of Articles - refusal to register transfer of shares (SR)—changes Articles so that directors have discretion to refuse to register a transfer of ownership of shares.

E32 Alteration of Articles - exclusion of statutory pre-emption rights (SR)—changes Articles so that the statutory rights of existing shareholders to be offered any shares which are to be allotted - before they are allotted to anyone else - are excluded.

E33 Alteration of Articles - quorum for general meeting (SR)—changes Articles so that if a quorum is not present at a general meeting the meeting be adjourned.

E34 Alteration of Articles - number of directors (SR)—changes Articles so that maximum and minimum numbers of directors may be varied.

E35 Alteration of Articles - alternate directors (SR)—changes Articles so that directors may specify that a proportion of their remuneration is paid to their alternate.

E36 Alteration of Articles - weighted voting rights (SR)—changes Articles so that directors (assuming they are shareholders) have weighted voting rights in order to prevent themselves from being removed from office.

E37 Alteration of Articles - authority to allot shares (SR)—changes Articles so that directors have authority to allot shares.

Standard Written Resolution — Form E01

Company Number: ______________

THE COMPANIES ACT
PRIVATE COMPANY LIMITED BY SHARES
WRITTEN RESOLUTION

OF

______________________ **LIMITED**

PASSED ON ______________________

We, the undersigned, being over 50% of the members of the company who, at the date of this resolution would be entitled to attend and vote at general meetings of the company, hereby unanimously resolve upon the following resolutions and agree that they shall be as valid and effective as if they had been passed as [ordinary/special] resolution (in the case of resolution 1) and [a special/ordinary] resolution (in the case of resolution 2) at a general meeting of the company duly convened and held.

[insert text of resolutions]____

____

Dated

____

____

____

Notes:

- *The directors must notify the company's auditors of the contents of the resolution at or before the time the resolution is supplied to the members (failure to do so can result in a fine) unless the company does not have an auditor(in which case they can still use the written resolution procedure) or the Articles permit a written resolution to be passed and do not require auditors.*
- *A written resolution must be signed by all members and whether there is an auditor to notify or not the resolution will be effective on the signature of the last member.*
- *The written resolution procedure cannot be used in two specified circumstances: a resolution to remove a director before the expiration of his period of office and a resolution to remove an auditor before the expiration of his term of office.*

Appointment of Director — Form E02

Company Number: ______________

THE COMPANIES ACT
PRIVATE COMPANY LIMITED BY SHARES
WRITTEN RESOLUTION

OF

______________________ **LIMITED**

PASSED ON ______________________

We, the undersigned, being over 50% of the members of the company who, at the date of this resolution would be entitled to attend and vote at general meetings of the company, hereby resolve upon the following resolution and agree that it shall be as valid and effective as if it had been passed as an ordinary resolution at a general meeting of the company duly convened and held.

That ________________________________ be appointed a director of the company[1]

Dated

____

____

____

[1] *File Companies House form AP01 within 14 days of appointment. Alter register of directors and if new director, or a person connected with them, is interested in shares in the company update the register of directors' interests upon receipt of the appropriate notification.*

Fixing of Maximum Number of Directors — Form E03

Company Number: ______________

THE COMPANIES ACT
PRIVATE COMPANY LIMITED BY SHARES
WRITTEN RESOLUTION

OF

______________________ **LIMITED**

PASSED ON ______________________

We, the undersigned, being over 50% of the members of the company who, at the date of this resolution would be entitled to attend and vote at general meetings of the company, hereby resolve upon the following resolution and agree that it shall be as valid and effective as if it had been passed as an ordinary resolution at a general meeting of the company duly convened and held.

That the maximum number of directors of the company shall be ____________________.

Dated

____

____

____

Reduction of Share Capital — Form E04

Company Number: ______________

THE COMPANIES ACT
PRIVATE COMPANY LIMITED BY SHARES
WRITTEN RESOLUTION

OF

______________________ **LIMITED**

PASSED ON ______________________

We, the undersigned, being over 50% of the members of the company who, at the date of this resolution would be entitled to attend and vote at general meetings of the company, hereby resolve upon the following resolution and agree that it shall be as valid and effective as if it had been passed as a special resolution at a general meeting of the company duly convened and held.

That in accordance with the Companies Act 2006 the share capital of the company be reduced[1] from £ ______________________, divided into __________ ordinary shares of [£1] each to £ ______________, divided into ____________ ordinary shares of [50p] each, and that such reduction be effected by cancelling paid up capital to the extent of [50p] on each of the shares of [£1] each in the capital of the company and reducing the nominal amount of each share whether issued or unissued from [£1] to [50p] accordingly.[2]

Dated

____

____

____

[1] *The rules governing a company's ability to reduce its share capital are complex and the procedure involves obtaining the consent of the court. This resolution should not therefore be used without first taking the advice of the company's solicitors.*

[2] *File resolution with Companies House.*

Allotment of Shares - Specific Form E05

Company Number:_______________

THE COMPANIES ACT
PRIVATE COMPANY LIMITED BY SHARES
WRITTEN RESOLUTION

OF

__________________________ **LIMITED**

PASSED ON ________________________

We, the undersigned, being over 50% of the members of the company who, at the date of this resolution would be entitled to attend and vote at general meetings of the company, hereby resolve upon the following resolution and agree that it shall be as valid and effective as if it had been passed as an ordinary resolution at a general meeting of the company duly convened and held.

That in accordance with the Companies Act 2006 the members authorise the directors to allot, or to grant any right to subscribe for or to convert any security into up to _________ ordinary shares of £ __________ each in the capital of the company for the purposes of ______________________________________ provided that such authority shall expire _________ months/years[1] from the date of the passing of the resolution and that the directors may make an offer or agreement before the expiry of such authority which would or might require shares to be allotted after the expiry of such authority.[2]

Dated

____

____

____

[1] *Unless the members pass a resolution to the contrary, the authority may only be given for up to a maximum period of five years from the date of the passing of this resolution.*

[2] *File resolution with Companies House.*

Allotment of Shares - General   Form E06

Company Number: _______________

THE COMPANIES ACT
PRIVATE COMPANY LIMITED BY SHARES
WRITTEN RESOLUTION

OF

_____________________________ LIMITED

PASSED ON _________________________

We, the undersigned, being over 50% of the members of the company who, at the date of this resolution would be entitled to attend and vote at general meetings of the company, hereby resolve upon the following resolution and agree that it shall be as valid and effective as if it had been passed as an ordinary resolution at a general meeting of the company duly convened and held.[1]

That in accordance with the Companies Act 2006 the members generally and unconditionally authorise the directors to allot, or to grant any right to subscribe for or to convert any security into up to ____________________ ordinary shares of _____________ each in the capital of the company provided that such authority shall expire ____ months/years from the date of the passing of this resolution[2] and that the directors may make an offer or agreement before the expiry of such authority which would or might require shares to be allotted after the expiry of such authority.

Dated

____

____

____

[1] *File resolution with Companies House*

[2] *The maximum period for which this authority may be given is five years but if the company has previously passed the relevant resolution this authority may be given for an indefinite period.*

Removal of Authority to Allot Shares — Form E07

Company Number: _______________

THE COMPANIES ACT
PRIVATE COMPANY LIMITED BY SHARES
WRITTEN RESOLUTION

OF

___________________________ **LIMITED**

PASSED ON ________________________

We, the undersigned, being over 50% of the members of the company who, at the date of this resolution would be entitled to attend and vote at general meetings of the company, hereby resolve upon the following resolution and agree that it shall be as valid and effective as if it had been passed as an ordinary resolution at a general meeting of the company duly convened and held.

That in accordance with the Companies Act 2006 the members hereby revoke the directors' authority to issue ordinary shares conferred on them by a resolution dated___________________________.

Dated

____

____

____

File resolution with Companies House within 15 days of passing.

Declaration of Dividend — Form E08

Company Number: ______________

THE COMPANIES ACT
PRIVATE COMPANY LIMITED BY SHARES
WRITTEN RESOLUTION

OF

______________________ **LIMITED**

PASSED ON ______________________

We, the undersigned, being over 50% of the members of the Company who, at the date of this resolution would be entitled to attend and vote at general meetings of the Company, hereby resolve upon the following resolution and agree that it shall be as valid and effective as if it had been passed as an ordinary resolution at a general meeting of the company duly convened and held.

That a dividend of ______________ p per share in respect of the year ended _________ be declared on the ordinary shares of ____________ each in the capital of the Company, payable on ______________________ to the holders of ordinary shares registered at the close of business on __________________ .[1]

Dated

____

____

____

[1] *Under the Model Articles shareholders cannot decide to pay themselves more than the directors have recommended, but they can decide to pay themselves less.*

Removal of Statutory Pre-Emption Rights - General Form E09

Company Number: _______________

THE COMPANIES ACT
PRIVATE COMPANY LIMITED BY SHARES
WRITTEN RESOLUTION

OF

__________________________ **LIMITED**

PASSED ON ________________________

We, the undersigned, being over 75% of the members of the company who, at the date of this resolution would be entitled to attend and vote at general meetings of the company, hereby resolve upon the following resolution and agree that it shall be as valid and effective as if it had been passed as a special resolution at a general meeting of the company duly convened and held.

That the Companies Act 2006, shall not apply to the allotment of shares pursuant to the general authority given by a resolution of the company dated _______________ and the directors may allot, grant options over or otherwise dispose of such shares to such persons, on such terms and in such manner as they see fit.[1]

Dated

____

____

____

[1] *File resolution with Companies House.*

Removal of Statutory Pre-Emption Rights in Respect of a Specified Allotment

Form E10

Company Number: ______________

THE COMPANIES ACT
PRIVATE COMPANY LIMITED BY SHARES
WRITTEN RESOLUTION

OF

______________________ **LIMITED**

PASSED ON ______________________

We, the undersigned, being over 75% of the members of the company who, at the date of this resolution would be entitled to attend and vote at general meetings of the company, hereby resolve upon the following resolution and agree that it shall be as valid and effective as if it had been passed as a special resolution at a general meeting of the company duly convened and held.

That the Companies Act 2006 shall not apply to the allotment of shares for the purposes of ____ pursuant to the authority given by a resolution[1] of the company dated ______________.

Dated

____

____

____

[1] *File resolution with Companies House. With the written resolution or the notice of meeting directors must send to members a written statement setting out their reasons for recommending this resolution, the amount to be paid to the company on the allotment and their justification for that amount. There are serious penalties if the directors issue a false, misleading or deceptive statement in these circumstances.*

Purchase of Own Shares — Form E11

Company Number: _______________

THE COMPANIES ACT
PRIVATE COMPANY LIMITED BY SHARES
WRITTEN RESOLUTION

OF

___________________________ **LIMITED**

PASSED ON ________________________

We, the undersigned, being over 75% of the members of the company who, at the date of this resolution would be entitled to attend and vote at general meetings of the company, hereby resolve upon the following resolution and agree that it shall be as valid and effective as if it had been passed as a special resolution at a general meeting of the company duly convened and held.[1]

That in accordance with the Companies Act 2006 the proposed contract for the purchase by the company of shares in the company held by ________________________________, a copy of which is attached to this resolution and marked 'A' for the purposes of identification, be approved.[2]

Dated

____

____

____

[1] *The purchase by a company of its own shares is allowed only in certain limited circumstances and the directors should not propose this resolution without first seeking the advice of the company's auditors and shareholders should take advice on the tax treatment of the money paid to them.*

[2] *The Articles must allow this. The contract must be available for inspection at the registered office for ten years after the passing of the resolution. Companies House form G169 must be presented to the Inland Revenue for stamping with the appropriate stamp duty and thereafter submitted to Companies House within 28 days of the purchase. The resolution should be submitted to Companies House within 15 days of being passed.*

Purchase of Own Shares from Capital — Form E12

Company Number: _______________

THE COMPANIES ACT
PRIVATE COMPANY LIMITED BY SHARES
WRITTEN RESOLUTION

OF

__________________________ **LIMITED**

PASSED ON ________________________

We, the undersigned, being over 75% of the members of the company who, at the date of this resolution would be entitled to attend and vote at general meetings of the company, hereby resolve upon the following resolution and agree that it shall be as valid and effective as if it had been passed as a special resolution at a general meeting of the company duly convened and held.[1]

That in accordance with the Companies Act 2006 the proposed contract for the purchase by the company of shares in the company held by ________________________________ a copy of which is attached to this resolution and marked 'A' for the purposes of identification be approved and that such purchase be financed out of capital.[2]

Dated

____

____

____

[1] *A company may only purchase its own shares out of capital (i.e. otherwise than from distributable profits or the proceeds of a fresh issue of shares) as a last resort. The rules governing such a purchase and the tax treatment of money paid to shareholders are complex and this resolution should not be proposed without first seeking the advice of the company's auditors and solicitors.*

[2] *The Articles must allow this. The contract must be available for inspection at the registered office for ten years after the passing of the resolution. Companies House form G169 must be presented to the Inland Revenue for stamping with the appropriate stamp duty and thereafter submitted to Companies House within 28 days of the purchase. The resolution should be submitted to Companies House within 15 days of being passed. Amend the register of members. Creditors must be notified by means of a notice in a national newspaper, and the relevant national edition of* The Gazette *(www.thegazette.co.uk). The directors must make a statutory declaration of solvency supported by a report given by the company's auditors.*

N.B. If this resolution is to be used at an general meeting delete reference to a copy of the contract being attached. The contract should instead be available for inspection at the registered office for 15 days before the meeting and at the meeting itself.

Bonus Issue — Form E13

Company Number: ______________

THE COMPANIES ACT
PRIVATE COMPANY LIMITED BY SHARES
WRITTEN RESOLUTION

OF

______________________ **LIMITED**

PASSED ON ______________________

We, the undersigned, being over 50% of the members of the company who, at the date of this resolution would be entitled to attend and vote at general meetings of the company, hereby resolve upon the following resolution and agree that it shall be as valid and effective as if it had been passed as an ordinary resolution at a general meeting of the company duly convened and held.

That the directors be authorised to capitalise the sum of £ __________ being part of the undivided profits of the company standing to the credit of the [profit and loss account] and to appropriate such sum to the holders of the ordinary shares of £1 each in the capital of the company as appearing in the register of members as at the close of business on ______________________ and that the directors be authorised and directed to apply such sum in paying up in full _____________ shares of £1 each in the capital of the company and to allot and distribute such new shares, credited as fully paid, to the holders of the shares in proportion to their existing holdings of ordinary shares of £1 each.

Dated

____

____

____

Once the resolution has been approved, the directors should resolve to allot the shares; the register of members and, where necessary, the register of directors' interests should be updated and share certificates issued. Form SH01 should be submitted to Companies House within one month of the allotment being made.

Approval of Substantial Property Transaction — Form E14

Company Number: ______________

THE COMPANIES ACT
PRIVATE COMPANY LIMITED BY SHARES
WRITTEN RESOLUTION

OF

______________________ **LIMITED**

PASSED ON ______________________

We, the undersigned, being over 50% of the members of the company who, at the date of this resolution would be entitled to attend and vote at general meetings of the company, hereby resolve upon the following resolution and agree that it shall be as valid and effective as if it had been passed as an ordinary resolution at a general meeting of the company duly convened and held.

That in accordance with the Companies Act the members approve the following transaction between the company and ____________________________________, a director of the company/a person connected with a director of the company.[1]

Dated

____

____

____

[1] These sections of the Companies Act requires any arrangement between a company and a director involving the transfer, either from the company to the director or from the director to the company, of a non-cash asset the value of which exceeds £100,000 or 10% of the company's net assets (provided it is not less than £2000) to be approved by the company's members.

Approval of Director's Remuneration — Form E15

Company Number: ______________

THE COMPANIES ACT
PRIVATE COMPANY LIMITED BY SHARES
WRITTEN RESOLUTION

OF

______________________ **LIMITED**

PASSED ON ______________________

We, the undersigned, being over 50% of the members of the company who, at the date of this resolution would be entitled to attend and vote at general meetings of the company, hereby resolve upon the following resolution and agree that it shall be as valid and effective as if it had been passed as an ordinary resolution at a general meeting of the company duly convened and held.

That the payment of £ __________ be paid to ______________________________
as remuneration on a __________________________ basis be approved.

Dated

____

____

____

Voluntary Liquidation - Solvent — Form E16

Company Number:______________

THE COMPANIES ACT
PRIVATE COMPANY LIMITED BY SHARES
WRITTEN RESOLUTION

OF

______________________ **LIMITED**

PASSED ON ______________________

We, the undersigned, being over 75% of the members of the company who, at the date of this resolution would be entitled to attend and vote at general meetings of the company, hereby resolve upon the following resolutions and agree that they shall be as valid and effective as if they had been passed as regards resolution no. 1 as a special resolution and as regards resolution no. 2 as an ordinary resolution at a general meeting of the company duly convened and held.[1]

1. That the Company being solvent, proceedings be initiated to effect a members' voluntary winding up.[2]
2. That ___________________________ be appointed as liquidator of the Company.

Dated

____

____

____

[1] *A statutory declaration of solvency must be made by the directors (or, if there are more than two directors, by a majority of them), at a board meeting, that they have made a full inquiry into the company's affairs and, having done so, have formed the opinion that the company will be able to pay its debts in full together with interest at the official rate within a period not exceeding 12 months from the commencement of the winding up. The declaration must be made within the five week period immediately preceding the passing of this resolution. It must be filed with Companies House within 15 days of the passing of the resolution.*

N.B. The directors should not make this declaration without taking the advice of the company's auditors and a licensed insolvency practitioner.

[2] *The special resolution must be advertised in the* London Gazette *(or the* Edinburgh Gazette *for Scottish-registered companies or the* Belfast Gazette *for those registered in Northern Ireland) within 14 days and filed at Companies House within 15 days. Notices for insertion in the Gazette need to be authenticated by either a solicitor, a chartered secretary, or a chartered or certified accountant. For Scottish-registered companies, notification of the liquidation also needs to be made to The Accountant in Bankruptcy, George House, 126 George Street, Edinburgh, EH2 4HH.*

Voluntary Liquidation - Insolvent — Form E17

Company Number: ______________

THE COMPANIES ACT
PRIVATE COMPANY LIMITED BY SHARES
WRITTEN RESOLUTION

OF

______________________ **LIMITED**

PASSED ON ______________________

We, the undersigned, being over 75% of the members of the company who, at the date of this resolution would be entitled to attend and vote at general meetings of the company, hereby resolve upon the following resolution and agree that it shall be as valid and effective as if it had been passed as a resolution at a general meeting of the company duly convened and held.

That, the company being unable to continue its business by reason of its liabilities[1], proceedings be initiated to effect a creditors' voluntary winding up.

Dated

____

____

____

[1] *The directors must take expert advice from a licensed insolvency practitioner as soon as it appears that the company may be unable to continue its business by reason of its liabilities.*

[2] *The special resolution must be advertised in the* London Gazette *(or the* Edinburgh Gazette *for Scottish-registered companies or the* Belfast Gazette *for those registered in Northern Ireland) within 14 days and filed at Companies House within 15 days. Notices for insertion in the Gazette need to be authenticated by either a solicitor, a chartered secretary, or a chartered or certified accountant. For Scottish-registered companies, notification of the liquidation also needs to be made to The Accountant in Bankruptcy, George House, 126 George Street, Edinburgh, EH2 4HH. A meeting of the company's creditors must be called within 14 days of the passing of the resolution and the creditors given at least seven days' notice of such meeting. The company should take legal advice concerning the contents of the notice to creditors and the procedure to be followed generally.*

Application for Administration Order — Form E18

Company Number: _______________

THE COMPANIES ACT
PRIVATE COMPANY LIMITED BY SHARES
WRITTEN RESOLUTION

OF

_______________________ **LIMITED**

PASSED ON _______________________

We, the undersigned, being over 50% of the members of the company who, at the date of this resolution would be entitled to attend and vote at general meetings of the company, hereby resolve upon the following resolution and agree that it shall be as valid and effective as if it had been passed as an ordinary resolution at a general meeting of the company duly convened and held.

That the company being/being likely to become unable[1] to pay its debts petition the court for an administration order in order to achieve _______________________.[2,3]

Dated

____

____

____

[1] *Delete as appropriate.*

[2] *Specify one of more of the outcomes (a) – (d) listed in footnote on Form C50.*

[3] *The resolution must be advertised in the relevant national edition of* The Gazette *(www.thegazette.co.uk) within 14 days and also in a newspaper in the area where the company has its principal place of business. Although the shareholders may pass this resolution, it is more usual for an application to be instigated by the directors without obtaining the approval of the shareholders (see Form C50).*

Reregistration as Public Company — Form E19

Company Number: ______________

THE COMPANIES ACT
PRIVATE COMPANY LIMITED BY SHARES
WRITTEN RESOLUTION

OF

______________________ **LIMITED**

PASSED ON ______________________

We, the undersigned, being 75% of the members of the company who, at the date of this resolution would be entitled to attend and vote at general meetings of the company, hereby resolve upon the following resolution and agree that it shall be as valid and effective as if it had been passed as a special resolution at a general meeting of the company duly convened and held.

That the company be reregistered as a public company as defined in the Companies Act 2006.[1]

That the name of the company be changed to ___________ Public Limited Company/Plc

That the Memorandum of Association of the company be amended :

a) by deleting in clause _____ the word 'Limited' and substituting 'Public Limited Company/Plc' therefor;
b) by inserting as a new clause the words 'The company is to be a public company'; an
c) by renumbering/relettering the remaining clauses of the Memorandum of Association.

That the regulations contained in the document marked 'A' be and are hereby adopted as the new Articles of Association of the company in place of all existing Articles of Association.

Dated

____

____

____

[1] *Send to Companies House: copy of resolution, application to reregister, new Memorandum and Articles of Association, copy of latest balance sheet, auditors' report and statutory declaration from director or secretary (for more details, see footnote to Form C44).The statutory reregistration fee should also be submitted to Companies House. The Articles of Association should be checked to ensure that any clauses relevant to a private company are removed, e.g. the ability to operate with only one director. The changes required to the Articles may be such that a new set of Articles may require to be adopted rather than making a series of textual changes to the existing Articles.*

Change of Company Name — Form E20

Company Number: ______________

THE COMPANIES ACT
PRIVATE COMPANY LIMITED BY SHARES
WRITTEN RESOLUTION

OF

______________________ **LIMITED**

PASSED ON ______________________

We, the undersigned, being 75% of the members of the company who, at the date of this resolution would be entitled to attend and vote at general meetings of the company, hereby resolve upon the following resolution and agree that it shall be as valid and effective as if it had been passed as a special resolution at a general meeting of the company duly convened and held.

That the name of the company be changed to ______________________________.[1]

Dated

____

____

____

[1] *File resolution with Companies House using Form NM01. Also send amended Memorandum and Articles and fee.*

Change of Articles — Form E21

Company Number: ______________

THE COMPANIES ACT
PRIVATE COMPANY LIMITED BY SHARES
WRITTEN RESOLUTION

OF

______________________ **LIMITED**

PASSED ON ______________________

We, the undersigned, being 75% of the members of the company who, at the date of this resolution would be entitled to attend and vote at general meetings of the company, hereby resolve upon the following resolution and agree that it shall be as valid and effective as if it had been passed as a special resolution at a general meeting of the company duly convened and held.

That the Articles of Association of the company be altered as follows:

1) By the deletion of Articles ___________ and _____________ and altering the subsequent numbering accordingly.

2) By the addition of the new Articles as set out in the attached document to be numbered _______ and _______ .

Dated

____

____

____

Adoption of New Articles of Association — Form E22

Company Number: ______________

THE COMPANIES ACT
PRIVATE COMPANY LIMITED BY SHARES
WRITTEN RESOLUTION

OF

______________________ **LIMITED**

PASSED ON ______________________

We, the undersigned, being 75% of the members of the company who, at the date of this resolution would be entitled to attend and vote at general meetings of the company, hereby resolve upon the following resolution and agree that it shall be as valid and effective as if it had been passed as a special resolution at a general meeting of the company duly convened and held.

That the document attached to this resolution be approved and adopted as the new Articles of Association of the company to the exclusion of its existing Articles.[1]

Dated

____

____

____

[1] *File new Articles and special resolution with Companies House.*

Change of Objects Form E23

Company Number: ________________

THE COMPANIES ACT
PRIVATE COMPANY LIMITED BY SHARES
WRITTEN RESOLUTION

OF

________________________ **LIMITED**

PASSED ON __________________________

We, the undersigned, being 75% of the members of the company who, at the date of this resolution would be entitled to attend and vote at general meetings of the company, hereby resolve upon the following resolution and agree that it shall be as valid and effective as if it had been passed as a special resolution at a general meeting of the company duly convened and held.

That the objects as set out in the document attached to this resolution be approved and adopted as the objects of the company in place of all existing objects and the company's Memorandum of Association be altered accordingly.[1]

Dated

____

____

____

[1] *File amended Memorandum and special resolution with Companies House.*

Approval of Compensation Payment — Form E24

Company Number: ______________

THE COMPANIES ACT
PRIVATE COMPANY LIMITED BY SHARES
WRITTEN RESOLUTION

OF

______________________ **LIMITED**

PASSED ON ______________________

We, the undersigned, being over 50% of the members of the company who, at the date of this resolution would be entitled to attend and vote at general meetings of the company, hereby resolve upon the following resolution and agree that it shall be as valid and effective as if it had been passed as an ordinary resolution at a general meeting of the company duly convened and held.

That a payment of £ _________ by the company to ______________________________ in consideration for his retirement as director of the company be approved.

Dated

____

____

____

Approval of Service Contract Exceeding Two Years' Duration Form E25

Company Number: ______________

THE COMPANIES ACT
PRIVATE COMPANY LIMITED BY SHARES
WRITTEN RESOLUTION

OF

______________________ **LIMITED**

PASSED ON ______________________

We, the undersigned, being over 50% of the members of the company who, at the date of this resolution would be entitled to attend and vote at general meetings of the company, hereby resolve upon the following resolution and agree that it shall be as valid and effective as if it had been passed as an ordinary resolution at a general meeting of the company duly convened and held.

That in accordance with the Companies Act 2006 the members consent to the granting of a service contract to ______________________________________ which exceeds two years in duration on the terms set out in the document attached hereto.[1]

Dated

____

____

____

[1] *Contract must be sent to each member at or before the time at which the resolution is supplied to him for signature. If this resolution is to be proposed at a general meeting, contract must be available for inspection by members at the meeting and for fifteen days prior to the meeting at the registered office.*

Ratification of Acts of Directors Beyond the Powers Delegated to Them under Company's Articles — Form E26

Company Number: _______________

THE COMPANIES ACT
PRIVATE COMPANY LIMITED BY SHARES
WRITTEN RESOLUTION

OF

____________________________ **LIMITED**

PASSED ON _________________________

We, the undersigned, being over 50% of the members of the company who, at the date of this resolution would be entitled to attend and vote at general meetings of the company, hereby resolve upon the following resolution and agree that it shall be as valid and effective as if it had been passed as an ordinary resolution at a general meeting of the company duly convened and held.

That all acts of the directors done prior to the date of this resolution be confirmed and ratified notwithstanding any matter that might otherwise cause their validity to be in doubt.[1]

Dated

____

____

____

[1] *This resolution ratifies any actions of the directors which are beyond the powers delegated to them in the company's Articles. If the directors have acted beyond the powers of the company as set out in the objects clause in its Memorandum of Association, this resolution is not appropriate and legal advice should be sought.*

Allowing of Director to Vote on Contracts where he has Personal Interest

Form E27

Company Number: ______________

THE COMPANIES ACT
PRIVATE COMPANY LIMITED BY SHARES
WRITTEN RESOLUTION

OF

______________________ **LIMITED**

PASSED ON ______________________

We, the undersigned, being over 50% of the members of the company who, at the date of this resolution would be entitled to attend and vote at general meetings of the company, hereby resolve upon the following resolution and agree that it shall be as valid and effective as if it had been passed as an ordinary resolution at a general meeting of the company duly convened and held.

That pursuant to regulation 96 of Table A (which is incorporated in the Articles of Association of the company by virtue of Article ______ of these Articles) ____, who is a director of this company, may vote on any resolution concerning a matter in which he has a personal interest notwithstanding Article _______ of the company's Articles of Association.

Dated

____

____

____

NB this form is for use only where the Table A regulations referred to in the resolution are presently incorporated in the company's Articles.

Proposal of Alteration of Articles - No Retirement by Rotation

Form E28

Company Number: ______________

THE COMPANIES ACT
PRIVATE COMPANY LIMITED BY SHARES
WRITTEN RESOLUTION

OF

______________________ **LIMITED**

PASSED ON ______________________

We, the undersigned, being 75% of the members of the company who, at the date of this resolution would be entitled to attend and vote at general meetings of the company, hereby resolve upon the following resolution and agree that it shall be as valid and effective as if it had been passed as an special resolution at a general meeting of the company duly convened and held.

That the company's Articles of Association be altered by the insertion of the wording set out below as new Article no.______ and the renumbering of the subsequent Articles accordingly/in substitution for existing Article no.______.[1]

The Directors shall not be required to retire by rotation.

Dated

____

____

____

[1] *Delete as appropriate. File resolution and copy of amended Articles with Companies House.*

Proposal of Alteration of Articles - Removal of Chairman's Casting Vote

Form E29

Company Number: ________________

THE COMPANIES ACT
PRIVATE COMPANY LIMITED BY SHARES
WRITTEN RESOLUTION

OF

______________________________ **LIMITED**

PASSED ON ____________________________

We, the undersigned, being 75% of the members of the company who, at the date of this resolution would be entitled to attend and vote at general meetings of the company, hereby resolve upon the following resolution and agree that it shall be as valid and effective as if it had been passed as an special resolution at a general meeting of the company duly convened and held.

That the company's Articles of Association be altered by the insertion of the wording set out below as new Article no.______ and the renumbering of the subsequent Articles accordingly/in substitution for existing Article no.______.[1]

The Chairman shall not have a casting vote.

Dated

____

____

____

[1] *Delete as appropriate. File resolution and copy of amended Articles with Companies House.*

Proposal of Alteration of Articles - Director Voting where Personal Interest

Form E30

Company Number: _______________

THE COMPANIES ACT
PRIVATE COMPANY LIMITED BY SHARES
WRITTEN RESOLUTION

OF

_________________________ **LIMITED**

PASSED ON _________________________

We, the undersigned, being 75% of the members of the company who, at the date of this resolution would be entitled to attend and vote at general meetings of the company, hereby resolve upon the following resolution and agree that it shall be as valid and effective as if it had been passed as an special resolution at a general meeting of the company duly convened and held.

That the company's Articles of Association be altered by the insertion of the wording set out below as new Article no.______ and the renumbering of the subsequent Articles accordingly/in substitution for existing Article no._______.[1]

> A director may vote at any meeting of the directors or of any committee of the directors on any resolution notwithstanding that it in any way concerns or relates to a matter in which he has, directly or indirectly, any kind of interest whatsoever and if he shall vote on any such resolution as aforesaid his vote shall be counted and in relation to any such resolution as aforesaid he shall (whether or not he shall vote on the same) be taken into account in calculating the quorum present at the meeting.

Dated

____

____

____

[1] *Delete as appropriate. File resolution and copy of amended Articles with Companies House.*

Proposal of Alteration of Articles - Refusal to Register Transfer of Shares

Form E31

Company Number: ______________

THE COMPANIES ACT
PRIVATE COMPANY LIMITED BY SHARES
WRITTEN RESOLUTION

OF

______________________ **LIMITED**

PASSED ON ______________________

We, the undersigned, being 75% of the members of the company who, at the date of this resolution would be entitled to attend and vote at general meetings of the company, hereby resolve upon the following resolution and agree that it shall be as valid and effective as if it had been passed as an special resolution at a general meeting of the company duly convened and held.

That the company's Articles of Association be altered by the insertion of the wording set out below as new Article no.______ and the renumbering of the subsequent Articles accordingly/in substitution for existing Article no.______.[1]

The directors may, in their absolute discretion and without assigning any reason, decline to register the transfer of a share, whether or not it is a fully paid share and regulation 24 in Table A shall not apply to the company.

Dated

____

____

____

[1] *Delete as appropriate. File resolution and copy of amended Articles with Companies House.*

Proposal of Alteration of Articles - Exclusion of Statutory Pre-Emption Rights

Form E32

Company Number: ______________

THE COMPANIES ACT
PRIVATE COMPANY LIMITED BY SHARES
WRITTEN RESOLUTION

OF

____________________ **LIMITED**

PASSED ON ______________________

We, the undersigned, being 75% of the members of the company who, at the date of this resolution would be entitled to attend and vote at general meetings of the company, hereby resolve upon the following resolution and agree that it shall be as valid and effective as if it had been passed as an special resolution at a general meeting of the company duly convened and held.

That the company's Articles of Association be altered by the insertion of the wording set out below as new Article no.______ and the renumbering of the subsequent Articles accordingly/in substitution for existing Article no.______.[1]

The Companies Act 2006, shall not apply to the company for this purpose.

Dated

____

____

____

[1] *Delete as appropriate. File resolution and copy of amended Articles with Companies House.*

Proposal of Alteration of Articles - Quorum for General Meeting

Form E33

Company Number: ________________

THE COMPANIES ACT
PRIVATE COMPANY LIMITED BY SHARES
WRITTEN RESOLUTION

OF

________________________ **LIMITED**

PASSED ON ________________________

We, the undersigned, being 75% of the members of the company who, at the date of this resolution would be entitled to attend and vote at general meetings of the company, hereby resolve upon the following resolution and agree that it shall be as valid and effective as if it had been passed as an special resolution at a general meeting of the company duly convened and held.

That the company's Articles of Association be altered by the insertion of the wording set out below as new Article no.______ and the renumbering of the subsequent Articles accordingly/in substitution for existing Article no.______.[1]

a) If a quorum is not present within half an hour from the time appointed for a general meeting the general meeting shall stand adjourned to the same day in the next week at the same time and place or to such other day and at such other time and place as the directors may determine and if at the adjourned general meeting a quorum is not present within half an hour from the time appointed such adjourned general meeting shall be dissolved.

b) Regulation 41 in Table A shall not apply to the company.

Dated

____

____

____

[1] *Delete as appropriate. File resolution and copy of amended Articles with Companies House.*

Proposal of Alteration of Articles - Number of Directors Form E34

Company Number: ______________

THE COMPANIES ACT
PRIVATE COMPANY LIMITED BY SHARES
WRITTEN RESOLUTION

OF

______________________ **LIMITED**

PASSED ON ______________________

We, the undersigned, being 75% of the members of the company who, at the date of this resolution would be entitled to attend and vote at general meetings of the company, hereby resolve upon the following resolution and agree that it shall be as valid and effective as if it had been passed as an special resolution at a general meeting of the company duly convened and held.

That the company's Articles of Association be altered by the insertion of the wording set out below as new Article no.______ and the renumbering of the subsequent Articles accordingly/in substitution for existing Article no._______.[1]

a) If appropriate, Regulation 64 in Table A does not apply to the company.

b) The maximum number and minimum number respectively of the Directors may be determined from time to time by Ordinary Resolution in General Meeting of the company. Subject to and in default of any such determination there shall be no maximum number of Directors and the minimum number of Directors shall be one. Whensoever the minimum number of Directors shall be one, a sole Director shall have authority to exercise all the powers and discretions by Table A/Model Articles and by these Articles expressed to be vested in the Directors generally and, where appropriate regulation 89 in Table A shall be modified accordingly.

Dated

____

____

____

[1] *Delete as appropriate. File resolution and copy of amended Articles with Companies House.*

Proposal of Alteration of Articles - Alternate Directors Form E35

Company Number: ______________

THE COMPANIES ACT
PRIVATE COMPANY LIMITED BY SHARES
WRITTEN RESOLUTION

OF

______________________ **LIMITED**

PASSED ON ______________________

We, the undersigned, being 75% of the members of the company who, at the date of this resolution would be entitled to attend and vote at general meetings of the company, hereby resolve upon the following resolution and agree that it shall be as valid and effective as if it had been passed as an special resolution at a general meeting of the company duly convened and held.

That the company's Articles of Association be altered by the insertion of the wording set out below as new Article no.______ and the renumbering of the subsequent Articles accordingly/in substitution for existing Article no.______.[1]

An alternate director shall not be entitled to receive any remuneration from the company, save that he may be paid by the company such part (if any) of the remuneration otherwise payable to his appointor as such appointor may by notice in writing to the company form time to time direct and Table A shall be modified accordingly.

Dated

____

____

____

[1] *Delete as appropriate. File resolution and copy of amended Articles with Companies House.*

Proposal of Alteration of Articles - Weighted Voting Rights Form E36

Company Number: ______________

THE COMPANIES ACT
PRIVATE COMPANY LIMITED BY SHARES
WRITTEN RESOLUTION

OF

______________________ **LIMITED**

PASSED ON ______________________

We, the undersigned, being 75% of the members of the company who, at the date of this resolution would be entitled to attend and vote at general meetings of the company, hereby resolve upon the following resolution and agree that it shall be as valid and effective as if it had been passed as a special resolution at a general meeting of the company duly convened and held.

That the company's Articles of Association be altered by the insertion of the wording set out below as new Article no. ______ and the renumbering of the subsequent Articles accordingly/in substitution for existing Article no.______.[1]

Every director for the time being of the company shall have the following rights:

a) if at any General Meeting a resolution is proposed to remove him from office, he shall be entitled to demand a poll and on that poll he shall have when voting against such resolution ____[2] votes for each share of which he is the holder; and

b) if at any General Meeting a poll is duly demanded on a resolution to delete or amend the provisions of this Article, he shall be entitled to demand a poll and on that poll he shall have when voting against such resolution ____[3] votes for each share of which he is the holder.

and Table A shall be modified accordingly.

Dated

____

____

____

[1] *Delete as appropriate. File resolution and copy of amended Articles with Companies House.*

Proposal of Alteration of Articles - Authority to Allot Shares

Form E37

Company Number: ________________

THE COMPANIES ACT
PRIVATE COMPANY LIMITED BY SHARES
WRITTEN RESOLUTION

OF

_________________________ **LIMITED**

PASSED ON _________________________

We, the undersigned, being 75% of the members of the company who, at the date of this resolution would be entitled to attend and vote at general meetings of the company, hereby resolve upon the following resolution and agree that it shall be as valid and effective as if it had been passed as an special resolution at a general meeting of the company duly convened and held.

That the company's Articles of Association be altered by the insertion of the wording set out below as new Article no.______ and the renumbering of the subsequent Articles accordingly/in substitution for existing Article no.______.[1]

The directors are generally and unconditionally authorised for the purposes of section 80 of the Companies Act to exercise any powers of the company to allot and grant rights to subscribe for or convert securities into share of the company up to the amount of the authorised share capital with which the company is incorporated at any time or times during the period of the five years from the date of incorporation and the directors may after that period allot any shares or grant any such rights under this authority in pursuance of an offer or agreement so to do made by the company within that period. The authority hereby given may at any time (subject to section 549 and 551 the Companies Act 2006) be renewed, revoked or varied by ordinary resolution of the company in general meeting.

Dated

____

____

____

[1] *Delete as appropriate. File resolution and copy of amended Articles with Companies House.*

Glossary

accounting reference date - the annual anniversary upon which a company's financial year ends.

accounting reference period - the period which ends on the accounting reference date.

administration order - the order of a court to appoint an administrator to manage a company in financial difficulties in an attempt to secure its survival or winding-up.

allotment - the appropriation of shares in the capital of the company to the applicants for those shares, by the board.

annual general meeting (AGM) - are no longer obligatory, but are still a good idea. Annual meetings of a company's shareholders to lay the annual accounts and directors' and auditors' reports before the shareholders and deal with other matters. Private companies can dispense with the need for AGMs by passing resolutions.

Annual Return - a prescribed form which must be filed annually with Companies House by a limited company, detailing the company's activities for the period up to the anniversary of the company's incorporation.

Articles of Association (or 'Articles') - the document containing the company's regulations for its internal management.

assets - anything owned with monetary value. This includes both real and personal property.

auditor - a person appointed to examine the accounts of a registered company and to report on them to company members.

authorised capital - this was the nominal capital which the company was authorised to issue by its Memorandum of Association. The concept of authorised capital has been abolished by the Companies Act 2006.

board - the directors of a company.

board meeting - a meeting of the directors.

company seal - a company may execute deeds by affixing its seal to them. There is no longer any requirement for a company to have seal and it may execute deeds by either two directors or a director and the company secretary signing the relevant document.

director - an officer of the company who manages company business and has a duty of care, skill and good faith.

elective resolution - a resolution which a private company was entitled to pass to reduce or remove certain administrative or formal requirements. It required the consent of all those shareholders entitled to vote. These no longer apply since the introduction of the Companies 2006.

extraordinary general meeting (EGM) - These are now simply called 'general meetings'. They were any meeting of company members other than the annual general meeting.

extraordinary resolution - These no longer apply. Any resolution that was 'extraordinary' is now regarded as a 'special resolution'. A resolution required to effect decisions in certain circumstances (e.g.

a creditors' winding up) and which requires a majority of not less than 75 per cent of the company members voting in person or by proxy at a general meeting.

general meeting - a meeting of shareholders. It may be an annual general meeting or general meeting where shareholders give their approval for transactions.

incorporate - to form a limited company by following procedures prescribed by law. On incorporation the limited company becomes a separate legal entity distinct from its owners.

insolvency - the inability of a company to meet its debts as they become due.

issued shares - shares which have been actually allotted by the company and in respect of which the allottees have been entered in the company's register of members.

member - person whose name has been entered in the company's register of members in respect of the shares he holds in the company.

Memorandum of Association - the company's charter enabling the outsider to establish the extent of the company's powers.

minutes - written records of formal proceedings of shareholders' and directors' meetings.

Model Articles – regulations published by the government for the management of a company.

ordinary resolution - a decision reached by a simple majority (more than 50 per cent) of company members voting in person or by proxy.

poll - ascertaining the will of the shareholders at a general meeting of the company by counting shareholders' votes according to the size of their share holdings.

pre-emption - the rights of existing shareholders granting them first option to acquire shares which are to be transferred or issued in proportion to their present share holding.

proxy - authorisation by a shareholder allowing another to vote his shares.

public limited company - a type of company incorporated by registration under the Companies Act which may offer its shares to the public (a private company cannot do this) and is subject to a number of additional requirements under the Companies Act.

quorum - the number of shareholders or directors necessary for vote a valid meeting.

registered office - the postal address of the company notified to Companies House.

remuneration - payment for services.

resolution - decision made by directors or shareholders in accordance with requisite majorities set out in Articles of Association. Resolutions may be approved in meetings or by written resolution.

share certificate - written and executed instrument showing who holds title to a particular share or series of shares.

service business - a business that sells service or advice instead of a tangible product.

shareholder - a holder of one or more shares in the capital of a company.

special resolution - a decision reached by not less than 75 per cent of company members voting in person or by proxy at a general meeting.

statutory books - the records that a company must keep as required by law. Changes must in many cases be notified to Companies House. The records should be kept at the company's registered office and are available to the public for inspection.

subscriber - a person who signs the Memorandum of Association and is issued the first shares in a new company.

Table A - for companies incorporated before 1 October 2009 these were the Model Articles. These have been replaced by Model Articles (see above).

written resolution - a resolution passed either by the shareholders or the directors of the company by signing a written form of the resolution rather than voting at a meeting of the company or at a meeting of the directors of the company.

APPENDIX 1

Examples of Registers

Register of Members

Name Alexander Palmer
Address 85 Preston Square
London SW6 5CN
Date of entry as shareholder 4-1-13 Date of cessation of membership

Date of Allotment OR Entry of Transfer	References in Register: Allotments	References in Register: Transfers	Number of shares	No. of Share Certificate	Amount paid or agreed to be considered as paid	Acquisitions
11-1-13	✔		1	1	£1	

Dividends to Alexander Palmer
Class of Share Ordinary Denomination £1 each

Disposals	Balance	Remarks
	£1	

Name Julia Etheridge
Address 16 St. George's Crescent
Reading RG7 9XY
Date of entry as shareholder 4-1-13 Date of cessation of membership

Date of Allotment ON Entry of Transfer	References in Register: Allotments	References in Register: Transfers	Number of shares	No. of Share Certificate	Amount paid or agreed to be considered as paid	Acquisitions
11-1-13	✔		1	2	£1	

Dividends to Julia Etheridge
Class of Share Ordinary Denomination £1 each

Disposals	Balance	Remarks
	£1	

Register of Directors

Surname (or Corporate Name) Palmer
Forenames(s) Alexander
any former Forenames or Surnames
Nationality British Date of Birth 3-2-55
Residential Address (or Registered or Principal Office 85 Preston Square
London SW6 5CN

Other Directorships None | Date of Resignation
Business Occupation Company Director
Date of Appointment 3-1-13 minute 11-1-13
Date of filing particulars 3-1-13
Date of Resignation or Cessation minute
Date of filing particulars

Surname (or Corporate Name) Etheridge
Forenames(s) Julia
any former Forenames or Surnames
Nationality British Date of Birth 29-9-57
Residential Address (or Registered or Principal Office 16 St. George's Crescent
Reading RG7 9XY

Other Directorships WA Limited | Date of Resignation
Business Occupation Sales Executive
Date of Appointment 3-1-13 minute 11-1-13
Date of filing particulars 3-1-13
Date of Resignation or Cessation minute
Date of filing particulars

Surname (or Corporate Name)
Forenames(s)
any former Forenames or Surnames
Nationality Date of Birth
Residential Address (or Registered or Principal Office

Other Directorships | Date of Resignation
Business Occupation
Date of Appointment minute
Date of filing particulars
Date of Resignation or Cessation minute
Date of filing particulars

Examples of Registers

Register of Secretaries

Surname (or Corporate Name) Palmer
Forenames(s) Alexander
any former Forenames or Surnames
Date of Appointment 3-1-13 minute 11-1-13
Date of filing particulars

Residential Address (or Registered or Principal Office) 85 Preston Square
London SW6 5CN
Date of Resignation or Cessation minute
Date of filing particulars

Surname (or Corporate Name)
Forenames(s)
any former Forenames or Surnames
Date of Appointment minute
Date of filing particulars

Residential Address (or Registered or Principal Office)
Date of Resignation or Cessation minute
Date of filing particulars

Surname (or Corporate Name)
Forenames(s)
any former Forenames or Surnames
Date of Appointment minute
Date of filing particulars

Residential Address (or Registered or Principal Office)
Date of Resignation or Cessation minute
Date of filing particulars

Surname (or Corporate Name)
Forenames(s)
any former Forenames or Surnames
Date of Appointment minute
Date of filing particulars

Residential Address (or Registered or Principal Office)
Date of Resignation or Cessation minute
Date of filing particulars

Surname (or Corporate Name)
Forenames(s)
any former Forenames or Surnames
Date of Appointment minute
Date of filing particulars

Residential Address (or Registered or Principal Office)
Date of Resignation or Cessation minute
Date of filing particulars

Register of Directors' Interests

Name and Address of Person Interested Alexander Palmer
85 Preston Square, London SW6 5CN

Entry		Date of		Nature of Event
No.	Date	Event	Notification	
1	4-1-13	3-1-13	4-1-13	Subscriber to memorandum of association

Classes of Share Capital or Debentures Ordinary shares
(a) 1 share of £1 each.
(b)

No. of shares involved		No. of Shares in which interested after event	Price consideration	Remarks
Acquisitions	Disposals			
1		1	£1	

Name and Address of Person Interested Julia Etheridge
16 St. George's Crescent, Reading RG7 9XY

Entry		Date of		Nature of Event
No.	Date	Event	Notification	
2	4-1-13	3-1-13	4-1-13	Subscriber to memorandum of association

Classes of Share Capital or Debentures Ordinary shares
(a) 1 share of £1 each.
(b)

No. of shares involved		No. of Shares in which interested after event	Price consideration	Remarks
Acquisitions	Disposals			
1		1	£1	

APPENDIX 2

Model Articles for Private Companies Limited by Shares

SCHEDULE 1

Regulation 2

MODEL ARTICLES FOR PRIVATE COMPANIES LIMITED BY SHARES

INDEX TO THE ARTICLES

PART 1

INTERPRETATION AND LIMITATION OF LIABILITY

PART 2

DIRECTORS

DIRECTORS' POWERS AND RESPONSIBILITIES

DECISION-MAKING BY DIRECTORS

APPOINTMENT OF DIRECTORS

PART 3

SHARES AND DISTRIBUTIONS

SHARES

DIVIDENDS AND OTHER DISTRIBUTIONS

CAPITALISATION OF PROFITS

PART 4

DECISION-MAKING BY SHAREHOLDERS

ORGANISATION OF GENERAL MEETINGS

VOTING AT GENERAL MEETINGS

PART 5

ADMINISTRATIVE ARRANGEMENTS

DIRECTORS' INDEMNITY AND INSURANCE

PART 1
INTERPRETATION AND LIMITATION OF LIABILITY

Defined terms

1. In the Articles, unless the context requires otherwise-
   'Articles' means the company's Articles of Association;
   'bankruptcy' includes individual insolvency proceedings in a jurisdiction other than England and Wales or Northern Ireland which have an effect similar to that of bankruptcy;
   'chairman' has the meaning given in Article 12;
   'chairman of the meeting' has the meaning given in Article 39;
   'Companies Acts' means the Companies Acts (as defined in section 2 of the Companies Act 2006), in so far as they apply to the company;
   'director' means a director of the company, and includes any person occupying the position of director, by whatever name called;
   'distribution recipient' has the meaning given in Article 31;
   'document' includes, unless otherwise specified, any document sent or supplied in electronic form;
   'electronic form' has the meaning given in section 1168 of the Companies Act 2006;
   'fully paid' in relation to a share, means that the nominal value and any premium to be paid to the company in respect of that share have been paid to the company;
   'hard copy form' has the meaning given in section 1168 of the Companies Act 2006;
   'holder' in relation to shares means the person whose name is entered in the register of members as the holder of the shares;
   'instrument' means a document in hard copy form;
   'ordinary resolution' has the meaning given in section 282 of the Companies Act 2006;
   'paid' means paid or credited as paid;
   'participate', in relation to a directors' meeting, has the meaning given in Article 10;
   'proxy notice' has the meaning given in Article 45;
   'shareholder' means a person who is the holder of a share;
   'shares' means shares in the company;
   'special resolution' has the meaning given in section 283 of the Companies Act 2006;
   'subsidiary' has the meaning given in section 1159 of the Companies Act 2006;
   'transmittee' means a person entitled to a share by reason of the death or bankruptcy of a shareholder or otherwise by operation of law; and
   'writing' means the representation or reproduction of words, symbols or other information in a visible form by any method or combination of methods, whether sent or supplied in electronic form or otherwise.
   Unless the context otherwise requires, other words or expressions contained in these Articles bear the same meaning as in the Companies Act 2006 as in force on the date when these Articles become binding on the company.

Liability of members

2. The liability of the members is limited to the amount, if any, unpaid on the shares held by them.

PART 2

DIRECTORS

DIRECTORS' POWERS AND RESPONSIBILITIES

Directors' general authority

3. Subject to the Articles, the directors are responsible for the management of the company's business, for which purpose they may exercise all the powers of the company.

Shareholders' reserve power

4. (1) The shareholders may, by special resolution, direct the directors to take, or refrain from taking, specified action.

(2) No such special resolution invalidates anything which the directors have done before the passing of the resolution.

Directors may delegate

5. (1) Subject to the Articles, the directors may delegate any of the powers which are conferred on them under the Articles-

(a) to such person or committee;

(b) by such means (including by power of attorney);

(c) to such an extent;

(d) in relation to such matters or territories; and

(e) on such terms and conditions;

as they think fit.

(2) If the directors so specify, any such delegation may authorise further delegation of the directors' powers by any person to whom they are delegated.

(3) The directors may revoke any delegation in whole or part, or alter its terms and conditions.

Committees

6. (1) Committees to which the directors delegate any of their powers must follow procedures which are based as far as they are applicable on those provisions of the Articles which govern the taking of decisions by directors.

(2) The directors may make rules of procedure for all or any committees, which prevail over rules derived from the Articles if they are not consistent with them.

DECISION-MAKING BY DIRECTORS

Directors to take decisions collectively

7. (1) The general rule about decision-making by directors is that any decision of the directors must be either a majority decision at a meeting or a decision taken in accordance with Article 8.

(2) If-

(a) the company only has one director, and

(b) no provision of the Articles requires it to have more than one director, the general rule does not apply, and the director may take decisions without regard to any of the provisions of the Articles relating to directors' decision-making.

Unanimous decisions

8. (1) A decision of the directors is taken in accordance with this Article when all eligible directors indicate to each other by any means that they share a common view on a matter.

(2) Such a decision may take the form of a resolution in writing, copies of which have been signed by each eligible director or to which each eligible director has otherwise indicated agreement in writing.

(3) References in this Article to eligible directors are to directors who would have been entitled to vote on the matter had it been proposed as a resolution at a directors' meeting.

(4) A decision may not be taken in accordance with this Article if the eligible directors would not have formed a quorum at such a meeting.

Calling a directors' meeting

9. (1) Any director may call a directors' meeting by giving notice of the meeting to the directors or by authorising the company secretary (if any) to give such notice.

(2) Notice of any directors' meeting must indicate-

(a) its proposed date and time;

(b) where it is to take place; and

(c) if it is anticipated that directors participating in the meeting will not be in the same place, how it is proposed that they should communicate with each other during the meeting.

(3) Notice of a directors' meeting must be given to each director, but need not be in writing.

(4) Notice of a directors' meeting need not be given to directors who waive their entitlement to notice of that meeting, by giving notice to that effect to the company not more than 7 days after the date on which the meeting is held. Where such notice is given after the meeting has been held, that does not affect the validity of the meeting, or of any business conducted at it.

Participation in directors' meetings

10. (1) Subject to the Articles, directors participate in a directors' meeting, or part of a directors' meeting, when-

(a) the meeting has been called and takes place in accordance with the Articles, and

(b) they can each communicate to the others any information or opinions they have on any particular item of the business of the meeting.

(2) In determining whether directors are participating in a directors' meeting, it is irrelevant where any director is or how they communicate with each other.

(3) If all the directors participating in a meeting are not in the same place, they may decide that the meeting is to be treated as taking place wherever any of them is.

Quorum for directors' meetings

11. (1) At a directors' meeting, unless a quorum is participating, no proposal is to be voted on, except a proposal to call another meeting.

(2) The quorum for directors' meetings may be fixed from time to time by a decision of the directors, but it must never be less than two, and unless otherwise fixed it is two.

(3) If the total number of directors for the time being is less than the quorum required, the directors must not take any decision other than a decision-

(a) to appoint further directors, or

(b) to call a general meeting so as to enable the shareholders to appoint further directors.

Chairing of directors' meetings

12. (1) The directors may appoint a director to chair their meetings.

(2) The person so appointed for the time being is known as the chairman.

(3) The directors may terminate the chairman's appointment at any time.

(4) If the chairman is not participating in a directors' meeting within ten minutes of the time at which it was to start, the participating directors must appoint one of themselves to chair it.

Casting vote

13. (1) If the numbers of votes for and against a proposal are equal, the chairman or other director chairing the meeting has a casting vote.

(2) But this does not apply if, in accordance with the Articles, the chairman or other director is not to be counted as participating in the decision-making process for quorum or voting purposes.

Conflicts of interest

14. (1) If a proposed decision of the directors is concerned with an actual or proposed transaction or arrangement with the company in which a director is interested, that director is not to be counted as participating in the decision-making process for quorum or voting purposes.

(2) But if paragraph (3) applies, a director who is interested in an actual or proposed transaction or arrangement with the company is to be counted as participating in the decision-making process for quorum and voting purposes.

(3) This paragraph applies when-

(a) the company by ordinary resolution disapplies the provision of the Articles which would otherwise prevent a director from being counted as participating in the decision-making process;

(b) the director's interest cannot reasonably be regarded as likely to give rise to a conflict of interest; or

(c) the director's conflict of interest arises from a permitted cause.

(4) For the purposes of this Article, the following are permitted causes-

(a) a guarantee given, or to be given, by or to a director in respect of an obligation incurred by or on behalf of the company or any of its subsidiaries;

(b) subscription, or an agreement to subscribe, for shares or other securities of the company or any of its subsidiaries, or to underwrite, sub-underwrite, or guarantee subscription for any such shares or securities; and

(c) arrangements pursuant to which benefits are made available to employees and directors or former employees and directors of the company or any of its subsidiaries which do not provide special benefits for directors or former directors.

(5) For the purposes of this Article, references to proposed decisions and decision-making processes include any directors' meeting or part of a directors' meeting.

(6) Subject to paragraph (7), if a question arises at a meeting of directors or of a committee of directors as to the right of a director to participate in the meeting (or part of the meeting) for voting or quorum purposes, the question may, before the conclusion of the meeting, be referred to the chairman whose ruling in relation to any director other than the chairman is to be final and conclusive.

(7) If any question as to the right to participate in the meeting (or part of the meeting) should arise in respect of the chairman, the question is to be decided by a decision of the directors at that meeting, for which purpose the chairman is not to be counted as participating in the meeting (or that part of the meeting) for voting or quorum purposes.

Records of decisions to be kept

15. The directors must ensure that the company keeps a record, in writing, for at least 10 years from the date of the decision recorded, of every unanimous or majority decision taken by the directors.

Directors' discretion to make further rules

16. Subject to the Articles, the directors may make any rule which they think fit about how they take decisions, and about how such rules are to be recorded or communicated to directors.

APPOINTMENT OF DIRECTORS

Methods of appointing directors

17. (1) Any person who is willing to act as a director, and is permitted by law to do so, may be appointed to be a director-

(a) by ordinary resolution, or

(b) by a decision of the directors.

(2) In any case where, as a result of death, the company has no shareholders and no directors, the personal representatives of the last shareholder to have died have the right, by notice in writing, to appoint a person to be a director.

(3) For the purposes of paragraph (2), where 2 or more shareholders die in circumstances rendering it uncertain who was the last to die, a younger shareholder is deemed to have survived an older shareholder.

Termination of director's appointment

18. A person ceases to be a director as soon as-

(a) that person ceases to be a director by virtue of any provision of the Companies Act 2006 or is prohibited from being a director by law;

(b) a bankruptcy order is made against that person;

(c) a composition is made with that person's creditors generally in satisfaction of that person's debts;

(d) a registered medical practitioner who is treating that person gives a written opinion to the company stating that that person has become physically or mentally incapable of acting as a director and may remain so for more than three months;

(e) by reason of that person's mental health, a court makes an order which wholly or partly prevents that person from personally exercising any powers or rights which that person would otherwise have;

(f) notification is received by the company from the director that the director is resigning from office, and such resignation has taken effect in accordance with its terms.

Directors' remuneration

19. (1) Directors may undertake any services for the company that the directors decide.
    (2) Directors are entitled to such remuneration as the directors determine-
        (a) for their services to the company as directors, and
        (b) for any other service which they undertake for the company.
    (3) Subject to the Articles, a director's remuneration may-
        (a) take any form, and
        (b) include any arrangements in connection with the payment of a pension, allowance or gratuity, or any death, sickness or disability benefits, to or in respect of that director.
    (4) Unless the directors decide otherwise, directors' remuneration accrues from day to day.
    (5) Unless the directors decide otherwise, directors are not accountable to the company for any remuneration which they receive as directors or other officers or employees of the company's subsidiaries or of any other body corporate in which the company is interested.

Directors' expenses

20. The company may pay any reasonable expenses which the directors properly incur in connection with their attendance at-
    (a) meetings of directors or committees of directors,
    (b) general meetings, or
    (c) separate meetings of the holders of any class of shares or of debentures of the company, or otherwise in connection with the exercise of their powers and the discharge of their responsibilities in relation to the company.

PART 3
SHARES AND DISTRIBUTIONS

SHARES

All shares to be fully paid up

21. (1) No share is to be issued for less than the aggregate of its nominal value and any premium to be paid to the company in consideration for its issue.
    (2) This does not apply to shares taken on the formation of the company by the subscribers to the company's Memorandum.

Powers to issue different classes of share

22. (1) Subject to the Articles, but without prejudice to the rights attached to any existing share, the company may issue shares with such rights or restrictions as may be determined by ordinary resolution.
    (2) The company may issue shares which are to be redeemed, or are liable to be redeemed at the option of the company or the holder, and the directors may determine the terms, conditions and manner of redemption of any such shares.

Company not bound by less than absolute interests

23. Except as required by law, no person is to be recognised by the company as holding any share upon any trust, and except as otherwise required by law or the Articles, the company is not in any way to be bound by or recognise any interest in a share other than the holder's absolute ownership of it and all the rights attaching to it.

Share certificates

24. (1) The company must issue each shareholder, free of charge, with one or more certificates in respect of the shares which that shareholder holds.
    (2) Every certificate must specify-
        (a) in respect of how many shares, of what class, it is issued;
        (b) the nominal value of those shares;
        (c) that the shares are fully paid; and
        (d) any distinguishing numbers assigned to them.
    (3) No certificate may be issued in respect of shares of more than one class.
    (4) If more than one person holds a share, only one certificate may be issued in respect of it.
    (5) Certificates must-
        (a) have affixed to them the company's common seal, or
        (b) be otherwise executed in accordance with the Companies Acts.

Replacement share certificates

25. (1) If a certificate issued in respect of a shareholder's shares is-
        (a) damaged or defaced, or
        (b) said to be lost, stolen or destroyed, that shareholder is entitled to be issued with a replacement certificate in respect of the same shares.
    (2) A shareholder exercising the right to be issued with such a replacement certificate-
        (a) may at the same time exercise the right to be issued with a single certificate or separate certificates;
        (b) must return the certificate which is to be replaced to the company if it is damaged or defaced; and
        (c) must comply with such conditions as to evidence, indemnity and the payment of a reasonable fee as the directors decide.

Share transfers

26. (1) Shares may be transferred by means of an instrument of transfer in any usual form or any other form approved by the directors, which is executed by or on behalf of the transferor.
    (2) No fee may be charged for registering any instrument of transfer or other document relating to or affecting the title to any share.
    (3) The company may retain any instrument of transfer which is registered.
    (4) The transferor remains the holder of a share until the transferee's name is entered in the register of members as holder of it.
    (5) The directors may refuse to register the transfer of a share, and if they do so, the instrument of transfer must be returned to the transferee with the notice of refusal unless they suspect that the proposed transfer may be fraudulent.

Transmission of shares

27. (1) If title to a share passes to a transmittee, the company may only recognise the transmittee as having any title to that share.
    (2) A transmittee who produces such evidence of entitlement to shares as the directors may properly require-
        (a) may, subject to the Articles, choose either to become the holder of those shares or to have them transferred to another person, and
        (b) subject to the Articles, and pending any transfer of the shares to another person, has the same rights as the holder had.

(3) But transmittees do not have the right to attend or vote at a general meeting, or agree to a proposed written resolution, in respect of shares to which they are entitled, by reason of the holder's death or bankruptcy or otherwise, unless they become the holders of those shares.

Exercise of transmittees' rights

28. (1) Transmittees who wish to become the holders of shares to which they have become entitled must notify the company in writing of that wish.

(2) If the transmittee wishes to have a share transferred to another person, the transmittee must execute an instrument of transfer in respect of it.

(3) Any transfer made or executed under this Article is to be treated as if it were made or executed by the person from whom the transmittee has derived rights in respect of the share, and as if the event which gave rise to the transmission had not occurred.

Transmittees bound by prior notices

29. If a notice is given to a shareholder in respect of shares and a transmittee is entitled to those shares, the transmittee is bound by the notice if it was given to the shareholder before the transmittee's name has been entered in the register of members.

DIVIDENDS AND OTHER DISTRIBUTIONS

Procedure for declaring dividends

30. (1) The company may by ordinary resolution declare dividends, and the directors may decide to pay interim dividends.

(2) A dividend must not be declared unless the directors have made a recommendation as to its amount. Such a dividend must not exceed the amount recommended by the directors.

(3) No dividend may be declared or paid unless it is in accordance with shareholders' respective rights.

(4) Unless the shareholders' resolution to declare or directors' decision to pay a dividend, or the terms on which shares are issued, specify otherwise, it must be paid by reference to each shareholder's holding of shares on the date of the resolution or decision to declare or pay it.

(5) If the company's share capital is divided into different classes, no interim dividend may be paid on shares carrying deferred or non-preferred rights if, at the time of payment, any preferential dividend is in arrear.

(6) The directors may pay at intervals any dividend payable at a fixed rate if it appears to them that the profits available for distribution justify the payment.

(7) If the directors act in good faith, they do not incur any liability to the holders of shares conferring preferred rights for any loss they may suffer by the lawful payment of an interim dividend on shares with deferred or non-preferred rights.

Payment of dividends and other distributions

31. (1) Where a dividend or other sum which is a distribution is payable in respect of a share, it must be paid by one or more of the following means-

(a) transfer to a bank or building society account specified by the distribution recipient either in writing or as the directors may otherwise decide;

(b) sending a cheque made payable to the distribution recipient by post to the distribution recipient at the distribution recipient's registered address (if the distribution recipient is a holder of the share), or (in any other case) to an address specified by the distribution recipient either in writing or as the directors may otherwise decide;

(c) sending a cheque made payable to such person by post to such person at such address as the distribution recipient has specified either in writing or as the directors may otherwise decide; or

(d) any other means of payment as the directors agree with the distribution recipient either in writing or by such other means as the directors decide.

(2) In the Articles, 'the distribution recipient' means, in respect of a share in respect of which a dividend or other sum is payable-

(a) the holder of the share; or

(b) if the share has two or more joint holders, whichever of them is named first in the register of members; or

(c) if the holder is no longer entitled to the share by reason of death or bankruptcy, or otherwise by operation of law, the transmittee.

No interest on distributions

32. The company may not pay interest on any dividend or other sum payable in respect of a share unless otherwise provided by-

(a) the terms on which the share was issued, or

(b) the provisions of another agreement between the holder of that share and the company.

Unclaimed distributions

33. (1) All dividends or other sums which are-

(a) payable in respect of shares, and

(b) unclaimed after having been declared or become payable, may be invested or otherwise made use of by the directors for the benefit of the company until claimed.

(2) The payment of any such dividend or other sum into a separate account does not make the company a trustee in respect of it.

(3) If-

(a) twelve years have passed from the date on which a dividend or other sum became due for payment, and

(b) the distribution recipient has not claimed it,

the distribution recipient is no longer entitled to that dividend or other sum and it ceases to remain owing by the company.

Non-cash distributions

34. (1) Subject to the terms of issue of the share in question, the company may, by ordinary resolution on the recommendation of the directors, decide to pay all or part of a dividend or other distribution payable in respect of a share by transferring non-cash assets of equivalent value (including, without limitation, shares or other securities in any company).

(2) For the purposes of paying a non-cash distribution, the directors may make whatever arrangements they think fit, including, where any difficulty arises regarding the distribution-

(a) fixing the value of any assets;

(b) paying cash to any distribution recipient on the basis of that value in order to adjust the rights of recipients; and

(c) vesting any assets in trustees.

Waiver of distributions

35. Distribution recipients may waive their entitlement to a dividend or other distribution payable in respect of a share by giving the company notice in writing to that effect, but if-

(a) the share has more than one holder, or

(b) more than one person is entitled to the share, whether by reason of the death or bankruptcy of one or more joint holders, or otherwise,

the notice is not effective unless it is expressed to be given, and signed, by all the holders or persons otherwise entitled to the share.

CAPITALISATION OF PROFITS

Authority to capitalise and appropriation of capitalised sums

36. (1) Subject to the Articles, the directors may, if they are so authorised by an ordinary resolution-

(a) decide to capitalise any profits of the company (whether or not they are available for distribution) which are not required for paying a preferential dividend, or any sum standing to the credit of the company's share premium account or capital redemption reserve; and

(b) appropriate any sum which they so decide to capitalise (a 'capitalised sum') to the persons who would have been entitled to it if it were distributed by way of dividend (the 'persons entitled') and in the same proportions.

(2) Capitalised sums must be applied-

(a) on behalf of the persons entitled, and

(b) in the same proportions as a dividend would have been distributed to them.

(3) Any capitalised sum may be applied in paying up new shares of a nominal amount equal to the capitalised sum which are then allotted credited as fully paid to the persons entitled or as they may direct.

(4) A capitalised sum which was appropriated from profits available for distribution may be applied in paying up new debentures of the company which are then allotted credited as fully paid to the persons entitled or as they may direct.

(5) Subject to the Articles the directors may-

(a) apply capitalised sums in accordance with paragraphs (3) and (4) partly in one way and partly in another;

(b) make such arrangements as they think fit to deal with shares or debentures becoming distributable in fractions under this Article (including the issuing of fractional certificates or the making of cash payments); and

(c) authorise any person to enter into an agreement with the company on behalf of all the persons entitled which is binding on them in respect of the allotment of shares and debentures to them under this Article.

PART 4

DECISION-MAKING BY SHAREHOLDERS

ORGANISATION OF GENERAL MEETINGS

Attendance and speaking at general meetings

37. (1) A person is able to exercise the right to speak at a general meeting when that person is in a position to communicate to all those attending the meeting, during the meeting, any information or opinions which that person has on the business of the meeting.

(2) A person is able to exercise the right to vote at a general meeting when-
(a) that person is able to vote, during the meeting, on resolutions put to the vote at the meeting, and
(b) that person's vote can be taken into account in determining whether or not such resolutions are passed at the same time as the votes of all the other persons attending the meeting.
(3) The directors may make whatever arrangements they consider appropriate to enable those attending a general meeting to exercise their rights to speak or vote at it.
(4) In determining attendance at a general meeting, it is immaterial whether any two or more members attending it are in the same place as each other.
(5) Two or more persons who are not in the same place as each other attend a general meeting if their circumstances are such that if they have (or were to have) rights to speak and vote at that meeting, they are (or would be) able to exercise them.

Quorum for general meetings

38. No business other than the appointment of the chairman of the meeting is to be transacted at a general meeting if the persons attending it do not constitute a quorum.

Chairing general meetings

39. (1) If the directors have appointed a chairman, the chairman shall chair general meetings if present and willing to do so.
(2) If the directors have not appointed a chairman, or if the chairman is unwilling to chair the meeting or is not present within ten minutes of the time at which a meeting was due to start-
(a) the directors present, or
(b) (if no directors are present), the meeting,
must appoint a director or shareholder to chair the meeting, and the appointment of the chairman of the meeting must be the first business of the meeting.
(3) The person chairing a meeting in accordance with this Article is referred to as 'the chairman of the meeting'.

Attendance and speaking by directors and non-shareholders

40. (1) Directors may attend and speak at general meetings, whether or not they are shareholders.
(2) The chairman of the meeting may permit other persons who are not-
(a) shareholders of the company, or
(b) otherwise entitled to exercise the rights of shareholders in relation to general meetings,
to attend and speak at a general meeting.

Adjournment

41. (1) If the persons attending a general meeting within half an hour of the time at which the meeting was due to start do not constitute a quorum, or if during a meeting a quorum ceases to be present, the chairman of the meeting must adjourn it.
(2) The chairman of the meeting may adjourn a general meeting at which a quorum is present if-
(a) the meeting consents to an adjournment, or
(b) it appears to the chairman of the meeting that an adjournment is necessary to protect the safety of any person attending the meeting or ensure that the business of the meeting is conducted in an orderly manner.

(3) The chairman of the meeting must adjourn a general meeting if directed to do so by the meeting.

(4) When adjourning a general meeting, the chairman of the meeting must-

(a) either specify the time and place to which it is adjourned or state that it is to continue at a time and place to be fixed by the directors, and

(b) have regard to any directions as to the time and place of any adjournment which have been given by the meeting.

(5) If the continuation of an adjourned meeting is to take place more than 14 days after it was adjourned, the company must give at least 7 clear days' notice of it (that is, excluding the day of the adjourned meeting and the day on which the notice is given)-

(a) to the same persons to whom notice of the company's general meetings is required to be given, and

(b) containing the same information which such notice is required to contain.

(6) No business may be transacted at an adjourned general meeting which could not properly have been transacted at the meeting if the adjournment had not taken place.

VOTING AT GENERAL MEETINGS

Voting: general

42. A resolution put to the vote of a general meeting must be decided on a show of hands unless a poll is duly demanded in accordance with the Articles.

Errors and disputes

43. (1) No objection may be raised to the qualification of any person voting at a general meeting except at the meeting or adjourned meeting at which the vote objected to is tendered, and every vote not disallowed at the meeting is valid.

(2) Any such objection must be referred to the chairman of the meeting, whose decision is final.

Poll votes

44. (1) A poll on a resolution may be demanded-

(a) in advance of the general meeting where it is to be put to the vote, or

(b) at a general meeting, either before a show of hands on that resolution or immediately after the result of a show of hands on that resolution is declared.

(2) A poll may be demanded by-

(a) the chairman of the meeting;

(b) the directors;

(c) two or more persons having the right to vote on the resolution; or

(d) a person or persons representing not less than one tenth of the total voting rights of all the shareholders having the right to vote on the resolution.

(3) A demand for a poll may be withdrawn if-

(a) the poll has not yet been taken, and

(b) the chairman of the meeting consents to the withdrawal.

(4) Polls must be taken immediately and in such manner as the chairman of the meeting directs.

Content of proxy notices

45. (1) Proxies may only validly be appointed by a notice in writing (a 'proxy notice') which-

(a) states the name and address of the shareholder appointing the proxy;
(b) identifies the person appointed to be that shareholder's proxy and the general meeting in relation to which that person is appointed;
(c) is signed by or on behalf of the shareholder appointing the proxy, or is authenticated in such manner as the directors may determine; and
(d) is delivered to the company in accordance with the Articles and any instructions contained in the notice of the general meeting to which they relate.

(2) The company may require proxy notices to be delivered in a particular form, and may specify different forms for different purposes.

(3) Proxy notices may specify how the proxy appointed under them is to vote (or that the proxy is to abstain from voting) on one or more resolutions.

(4) Unless a proxy notice indicates otherwise, it must be treated as-
(a) allowing the person appointed under it as a proxy discretion as to how to vote on any ancillary or procedural resolutions put to the meeting, and
(b) appointing that person as a proxy in relation to any adjournment of the general meeting to which it relates as well as the meeting itself.

Delivery of proxy notices

46. (1) A person who is entitled to attend, speak or vote (either on a show of hands or on a poll) at a general meeting remains so entitled in respect of that meeting or any adjournment of it, even though a valid proxy notice has been delivered to the company by or on behalf of that person.

(2) An appointment under a proxy notice may be revoked by delivering to the company a notice in writing given by or on behalf of the person by whom or on whose behalf the proxy notice was given.

(3) A notice revoking a proxy appointment only takes effect if it is delivered before the start of the meeting or adjourned meeting to which it relates.

(4) If a proxy notice is not executed by the person appointing the proxy, it must be accompanied by written evidence of the authority of the person who executed it to execute it on the appointor's behalf.

Amendments to resolutions

47. (1) An ordinary resolution to be proposed at a general meeting may be amended by ordinary resolution if-
(a) notice of the proposed amendment is given to the company in writing by a person entitled to vote at the general meeting at which it is to be proposed not less than 48 hours before the meeting is to take place (or such later time as the chairman of the meeting may determine), and
(b) the proposed amendment does not, in the reasonable opinion of the chairman of the meeting, materially alter the scope of the resolution.

(2) A special resolution to be proposed at a general meeting may be amended by ordinary resolution, if-
(a) the chairman of the meeting proposes the amendment at the general meeting at which the resolution is to be proposed, and
(b) the amendment does not go beyond what is necessary to correct a grammatical or other non-substantive error in the resolution.

(3) If the chairman of the meeting, acting in good faith, wrongly decides that an amendment to a resolution is out of order, the chairman's error does not invalidate the vote on that resolution.

PART 5
ADMINISTRATIVE ARRANGEMENTS

Means of communication to be used

48. (1) Subject to the Articles, anything sent or supplied by or to the company under the Articles may be sent or supplied in any way in which the Companies Act 2006 provides for documents or information which are authorised or required by any provision of that Act to be sent or supplied by or to the company.

(2) Subject to the Articles, any notice or document to be sent or supplied to a director in connection with the taking of decisions by directors may also be sent or supplied by the means by which that director has asked to be sent or supplied with such notices or documents for the time being.

(3) A director may agree with the company that notices or documents sent to that director in a particular way are to be deemed to have been received within a specified time of their being sent, and for the specified time to be less than 48 hours.

Company seals

49. (1) Any common seal may only be used by the authority of the directors.

(2) The directors may decide by what means and in what form any common seal is to be used.

(3) Unless otherwise decided by the directors, if the company has a common seal and it is affixed to a document, the document must also be signed by at least one authorised person in the presence of a witness who attests the signature.

(4) For the purposes of this Article, an authorised person is-

(a) any director of the company;

(b) the company secretary (if any); or

(c) any person authorised by the directors for the purpose of signing documents to which the common seal is applied.

No right to inspect accounts and other records

50. Except as provided by law or authorised by the directors or an ordinary resolution of the company, no person is entitled to inspect any of the company's accounting or other records or documents merely by virtue of being a shareholder.

Provision for employees on cessation of business

51. The directors may decide to make provision for the benefit of persons employed or formerly employed by the company or any of its subsidiaries (other than a director or former director or shadow director) in connection with the cessation or transfer to any person of the whole or part of the undertaking of the company or that subsidiary.

DIRECTORS' INDEMNITY AND INSURANCE

Indemnity

52. (1) Subject to paragraph (2), a relevant director of the company or an associated company may be indemnified out of the company's assets against-

(a) any liability incurred by that director in connection with any negligence, default, breach of duty or breach of trust in relation to the company or an associated company,

(b) any liability incurred by that director in connection with the activities of the company or an associated company in its capacity as a trustee of an occupational pension scheme (as defined in section 235(6) of the Companies Act 2006),

(c) any other liability incurred by that director as an officer of the company or an associated company.

(2) This Article does not authorise any indemnity which would be prohibited or rendered void by any provision of the Companies Acts or by any other provision of law.

(3) In this Article-

(a) companies are associated if one is a subsidiary of the other or both are subsidiaries of the same body corporate, and

(b) a 'relevant director' means any director or former director of the company or an associated company.

Insurance

53. (1) The directors may decide to purchase and maintain insurance, at the expense of the company, for the benefit of any relevant director in respect of any relevant loss.

(2) In this Article-

(a) a 'relevant director' means any director or former director of the company or an associated company,

(b) a 'relevant loss' means any loss or liability which has been or may be incurred by a relevant director in connection with that director's duties or powers in relation to the company, any associated company or any pension fund or employees' share scheme of the company or associated company, and

(c) companies are associated if one is a subsidiary of the other or both are subsidiaries of the same body corporate.

Notes